NUCLEAR POWER PLANT PERSONNEL TRAINING AND ITS EVALUATION

A Guidebook

The following States are Members of the International Atomic Energy Agency:

AFGHANISTAN	HUNGARY	PERU
ALBANIA	ICELAND	PHILIPPINES
ALGERIA	INDIA	POLAND
ARGENTINA	INDONESIA	PORTUGAL
ARMENIA	IRAN,	QATAR
AUSTRALIA	ISLAMIC REPUBLIC OF	ROMANIA
AUSTRIA	IRAQ	RUSSIAN FEDERATION
BANGLADESH	IRELAND	SAUDI ARABIA
BELARUS	ISRAEL	SENEGAL
BELGIUM	ITALY	SIERRA LEONE
BOLIVIA	JAMAICA	SINGAPORE
BOSNIA AND	JAPAN	SLOVAKIA
HERZEGOVINA	JORDAN	SLOVENIA
BRAZIL	KAZAKHSTAN	SOUTH AFRICA
BULGARIA	KENYA	SPAIN
CAMBODIA	KOREA, REPUBLIC OF	SRI LANKA
CAMEROON	KUWAIT	SUDAN
CANADA	LEBANON	SWEDEN
CHILE	LIBERIA	SWITZERLAND
CHINA	LIBYAN ARAB JAMAHIRIYA	SYRIAN ARAB REPUBLIC
COLOMBIA	LIECHTENSTEIN	THAILAND
COSTA RICA	LITHUANIA	THE FORMER YUGOSLAV
COTE D'IVOIRE	LUXEMBOURG	REPUBLIC OF MACEDONIA
CROATIA	MADAGASCAR	TUNISIA
CUBA	MALAYSIA	TURKEY
CYPRUS	MALI	UGANDA
CZECH REPUBLIC	MARSHALL ISLANDS	UKRAINE
DENMARK	MAURITIUS	UNITED ARAB EMIRATES
DOMINICAN REPUBLIC	MEXICO	UNITED KINGDOM OF
ECUADOR	MONACO	GREAT BRITAIN AND
EGYPT	MONGOLIA	NORTHERN IRELAND
EL SALVADOR	MOROCCO	UNITED REPUBLIC
ESTONIA	MYANMAR	OF TANZANIA
ETHIOPIA	NAMIBIA	UNITED STATES OF AMERICA
FINLAND	NETHERLANDS	URUGUAY
FRANCE	NEW ZEALAND	UZBEKISTAN
GABON	NICARAGUA	VENEZUELA
GERMANY	NIGER	VIET NAM
GHANA	NIGERIA	YEMEN
GREECE	NORWAY	YUGOSLAVIA
GUATEMALA	PAKISTAN	ZAIRE
HAITI	PANAMA	ZAMBIA
HOLY SEE	PARAGUAY	ZIMBABWE

The Agency's Statute was approved on 23 October 1956 by the Conference on the Statute of the IAEA held at United Nations Headquarters, New York; it entered into force on 29 July 1957. The Headquarters of the Agency are situated in Vienna. Its principal objective is "to accelerate and enlarge the contribution of atomic energy to peace, health and prosperity throughout the world".

Printed by the IAEA in Austria
May 1996
STI/DOC/010/380

TECHNICAL REPORTS SERIES No. 380

NUCLEAR POWER PLANT PERSONNEL TRAINING AND ITS EVALUATION

A Guidebook

INTERNATIONAL ATOMIC ENERGY AGENCY
VIENNA, 1996

VIC Library Cataloguing in Publication Data

Nuclear power plant personnel training and its evaluation : a guidebook. —
    Vienna : International Atomic Energy Agency, 1996.
        p. ; 24 cm. — (Technical reports series, ISSN 0074-1914 ; 380)
    STI/DOC/010/380
    ISBN 92-0-101496-1
    Includes bibliographical references.

    1. Nuclear power plants—Employees—Training of. I. International
Atomic Energy Agency. II. Series: Technical reports series (International
Atomic Energy Agency) ; 380.

VICL   96-00145

FOREWORD

A central challenge and requirement for ensuring the safety and reliability of nuclear power is to attain and maintain the qualification and competence of nuclear power plant (NPP) personnel, which includes operations, maintenance, management and technical support personnel. The objectives of safety and reliability cannot be achieved solely by the quality of equipment and hardware, but depend critically also on sufficient numbers of personnel having the necessary qualification and competence to carry out their tasks and responsibilities.

The Guidebook on Nuclear Power Plant Personnel Training and its Evaluation recommends the use of the Systematic Approach to Training (SAT) for NPP personnel. The Guidebook is a revision and updating of the IAEA Guidebook on Training to Establish and Maintain the Qualification and Competence of Nuclear Power Plant Operations Personnel (IAEA-TECDOC-525) and incorporates the experience gained worldwide since the publication of IAEA-TECDOC-525 in 1989.

SAT is now recognized as the international best practice for attaining and maintaining the qualification and competence of NPP personnel and for the quality assurance of training. SAT can and should be adapted to suit the specific requirements and conditions of individual countries and NPPs, utilizing and building upon existing capabilities. It also incorporates aspects that promote a safety culture among staff and management. Regulatory bodies in a number of countries mandate or strongly recommend the use of SAT based training for NPP personnel.

Experience has shown that, to attain professional competence, SAT should comprise training to achieve both the necessary technical and human factors competencies. Thus, the new Guidebook emphasizes a broader concept of competence which includes not only technical knowledge and skills but also knowledge, skills and attitudes related to human factors. In addition to the training of operating personnel, the Guidebook deals with the role and responsibilities of management; the training of management and maintenance personnel; organizations involved in training; and more effective and efficient methods of SAT analysis. It also emphasizes and covers evaluation of the overall training process, as well as providing examples of SAT applications.

The Guidebook will prove especially useful for, and is addressed primarily to: nuclear power operating organizations establishing or upgrading their NPP personnel training systems; regulatory personnel responsible for setting requirements and/or evaluating NPP personnel training; and organizations (within or outside the operating organization) responsible for the development, implementation and evaluation of training programmes for NPP personnel.

This Technical Report was initially drafted by the IAEA Secretariat working with a small group of consultants. Further development of the document incorporated comments from ten Member States at four Consultants Meetings. The document was widely circulated for additional comments. The final draft was prepared by S. Birnie (UK), P. Billard (France), A.Yu. Kazennov (Russian Federation), T. Mazour (USA), P. Pianarosa (Canada) and F. Mautner Markhof of the Nuclear Power Engineering Section, Division of Nuclear Power, the IAEA officer responsible for this report. The final revision was reviewed and approved at the Advisory Group Meeting in which experts from 16 Member States and the CEC participated.

The IAEA acknowledges with thanks the extrabudgetary contribution of the United States Government for the project to develop the Guidebook. Appreciation is also expressed to all those who participated in the preparation of the Guidebook and to Member States for their support in providing experts from operating organizations, NPPs, training organizations and regulatory bodies to assist the IAEA in this work.

CONTENTS

1. INTRODUCTION

1.1. PURPOSE OF GUIDEBOOK

One of the most critical requirements for safe and reliable nuclear power plant (NPP) operations and maintenance is the availability of sufficient numbers of competent personnel. Experience has shown that, in addition to the quality of the design and equipment, personnel competence is essential to ensure safety and reliability.

This Guidebook on Nuclear Power Plant Personnel Training and its Evaluation constitutes the recommendations of the IAEA on the use of the Systematic Approach to Training (SAT) for the training of NPP personnel. The Guidebook is a revision of IAEA-TECDOC-525, Guidebook on Training to Establish and Maintain the Qualification and Competence of Nuclear Power Plant Operations Personnel. This new Guidebook incorporates the results of nearly six years of worldwide experience in the use of SAT for NPP personnel training since the publication, in 1989, of IAEA-TECDOC-525.

SAT is an approach to training that provides a logical progression from the identification of the competencies required to perform a job to the development and implementation of training to achieve these competencies, and the subsequent evaluation of this training.

In this context, NPP personnel includes those performing operating, maintenance, technical support and management jobs.

Experience has shown that SAT is the best method now available for producing fully auditable training programmes for NPP personnel. These programmes aim at developing competent personnel and at ensuring that their qualifications and competence are maintained. It is recognized and emphasized that SAT *is not an end in itself but the most effective means* of achieving the level of competence required for NPP personnel.

The Guidebook is addressed primarily to:

- Nuclear power operating organizations wishing to establish or improve the training systems for NPP personnel;
- Regulatory personnel responsible for setting requirements and/or evaluating NPP personnel training;
- Organizations (within or outside the operating organization) involved in the development, implementation and evaluation of training programmes for NPP personnel.

1

1.2. SCOPE OF GUIDEBOOK

1.2.1. Approach to training

The Guidebook addresses what SAT is and gives examples of SAT applications. Furthermore, it provides the basis for the transfer of knowledge to countries seeking to develop or upgrade their training for NPP personnel.

On the basis of experience gained worldwide, it is now agreed that SAT should be considered as a broad integrated approach emphasizing not only technical knowledge and skills but also human factors knowledge, skills and attitudes (KSAs). In this way, all of the requirements for attaining and maintaining personnel competence can be met. This also promotes and strengthens safety culture and quality culture, which should be fostered throughout the initial and continuing training programmes, as well as through other means.

The Guidebook places emphasis on such areas as: maintenance training, the role and responsibilities of management, emergency preparedness training, organizational aspects of training, and human factors KSAs required for competence.

In particular, this Guidebook provides an alternative to job and task analysis for the analysis phase of SAT. This alternative, referred to as job competencies analysis, does not require such large amounts of time, financial and human resources. The method permits, where appropriate, a streamlined analysis based on identifying competencies (groups of KSAs) associated with a given job.

The critical role of operating personnel has been rightly emphasized by every country with a nuclear power programme, and training programmes and resources have reflected this. Despite the fact that the competence of maintenance personnel is essential for reducing the frequency of events connected with equipment failures and other maintenance-related causes, maintenance training has received far less attention and resources to date. There is now widespread agreement that training for maintenance personnel must be improved through, among other things, the use of SAT to develop these training programmes or to bring them up to date.

1.2.2. Evaluation of training programmes

This Guidebook contains the IAEA's recommendations and guidance on the overall evaluation of the entire training process including the organization and management of training.

The evaluation phase of SAT includes:

- Feedback from plant operational experience and industry wide operational experience;
- Reports from inspections and audits;

- Feedback from plant supervisors, training programme graduates, instructors and trainees;
- Observation of training and plant activities and other internal reviews.

Evaluation comprises not only internal evaluation by the operating organization but also independent (external) team review by experts not in the operating organization using agreed criteria, as well as regulatory inspections. The results of evaluation are used to confirm, improve or modify the training programmes and training process. Additionally, necessary plant improvements may be identified.

1.2.3. Quality assurance of training programmes

SAT has inherent quality assurance (QA) features, and its use, therefore, leads to an auditable training system. The implementation of SAT also assists NPP management to achieve QA of training. SAT is thus a valuable tool in the overall NPP QA programme. It must be emphasized, however, that neither SAT nor its QA features can be successfully implemented without the full support of upper level NPP management.

1.2.4. Introduction and use of SAT

The introduction of SAT will require adequate numbers of personnel having the necessary technical and teaching competence.

SAT is widely used or being introduced in almost all countries with major nuclear power programmes. It is a flexible approach which can and should be adapted to the specific needs, conditions and resources of individual NPPs.

For implementing a SAT based training programme, this Guidebook provides important recommendations and information. Nevertheless, it is not intended that the Guidebook alone should be sufficient for this purpose. It needs to be used in conjunction with expert advice and assistance as well as know-how transfer through technical visits of NPP and other training staff involved.

To ensure the widest possible utilization of this Guidebook, a summary has been prepared and is being published in the official languages of the IAEA.

2. THE ROLE OF MANAGEMENT

This section is primarily addressed to the management of the operating organization and to plant management. It describes the role and responsibilities of management for the training and competence of NPP personnel.

2.1. RESPONSIBILITIES

The operating organization is responsible for the recruitment and training of NPP personnel and for the definition of competence levels. Only qualified persons shall be entrusted with functions important to safety. These functions and the related duties and responsibilities shall be clearly indicated in the description of the operating organization. The responsibility for ensuring that individuals are appropriately qualified and remain so rests with the operating organization (for reference, see IAEA Safety Guide 50-SG-01, Rev. 1).

These responsibilities are generally delegated by the operating organization to the plant manager. In general, regulators hold plant managers accountable for discharging these responsibilities.

The operating organization management is responsible for providing the financial and organizational means to fulfil the goals of NPP personnel training in an efficient and effective manner.

The plant manager has the overall responsibility for, and plays an important role in, the development and implementation of training programmes to ensure the qualification and competence of NPP personnel. These responsibilities include: establishing qualification requirements, meeting regulatory requirements, monitoring training programmes, providing necessary resources, maintaining competence, and effective human resources policy and management.

While the plant manager is ultimately responsible for NPP personnel performance, he defines and assigns in writing many of these responsibilities to plant departments and then holds the managers of these departments accountable for carrying out their assigned responsibilities. These managers should then develop precise job descriptions for all positions within their departmental areas, detailing responsibilities and standards of performance for each position.

The attitude of plant management towards the training and qualification of NPP personnel is another important factor for safe and reliable plant operation. If plant management does not actively support and reinforce the standards for safety and quality established for training programmes, these standards will not be applied at the NPP. For example, if safety training teaches trainees the proper use of personnel protective equipment but these practices are not enforced in the plant, then the effectiveness of all training and qualification programmes is reduced. This example also illustrates the relationship between training and safety culture. This relationship will be discussed in more detail in Section 2.5.

2.2. TRAINING POLICY

The IAEA's Report on Safety Culture, INSAG-4, states that actions by individuals in any activity are shaped by requirements imposed at a higher level. At NPPs, these requirements are stated as policies. It is necessary that the operating organization formulate and promulgate an overall training policy — in the form of a written document — dealing with the training, qualifications and performance of NPP personnel. This policy is the commitment by the operating organization and the NPP to personnel training and an acknowledgement of the critical role of training for the safe, reliable operation and maintenance of the NPP. This section describes the characteristics of such a policy.

The operating organization should clearly define the responsibilities for all aspects of the training process. This information on responsibilities should be included in the training policy and in the written procedures for SAT.

For organizations which operate several NPPs, the overall training policy is formulated at the operating organization level, with individual NPP policies based on the overall policy. Policies at all levels need to be consistent with the overall policy and with each other, the policy at each level being based upon that of the level above. Also, in some countries, there are national level policies on which individual NPP training policies must be based.

The training policy should be consistent with (and may also refer to) other policies, such as those for:

- Safety
- Quality
- Human resources
- Environmental protection
- Recruitment of personnel
- Career development and motivation of personnel
- Cooperation to create the necessary plant attitudes.

Training policy should be based upon the longer term needs and goals of the NPP. However, the policy should be evaluated at regular intervals in order to ensure that it is consistent with current needs and goals. Factors which can change a training policy include: operational experience and events at the NPPs of the operating organization or at other plants, significant backfitting of the plant, commissioning or decommissioning of a plant, NPP reorganization, and modifications in the national education system.

The training policy should reinforce the principle that training organizations exist only to serve the needs of the plant(s) which they support, and that the training process must be flexible and responsive enough to keep pace with organizational and technological changes, and with national and international operational experience.

There must be regular and mutually co-operative interactions and communications between the plant organization and the training organization, including the use of plant personnel for specific training functions.

2.3. COMPONENTS OF A TRAINING POLICY

The essential components of a training policy are the following:

- Goals and scope of training;
- Responsibilities for training;
- Monitoring, evaluation and control of the performance of training.

2.3.1. Goals and scope of the training policy

The internationally agreed requirement for all personnel whose work may have an impact on safe and efficient NPP operation and maintenance is that they are qualified for, and competent to perform, their jobs, on the basis of education, training and experience. SAT is now recognized worldwide as the best method of ensuring that personnel are appropriately qualified, because it:

- Identifies all the training needed for achieving competence;
- Provides QA of training and thus builds quality into training and qualification programmes;
- Provides tools for management to monitor, evaluate and control continually the effectiveness of training provided and the competence of NPP personnel.

It is recommended that the overall training policy or other high level document of the operating organization require the use of SAT for training personnel whose jobs impact safe and reliable NPP operation.

It is recognized that NPPs have differing requirements for their training programmes, which will need to be reflected in the training policy. For example, there are different NPP approaches for the use of outside contractors for maintenance of equipment. Some NPPs rely almost totally on their own employees for the performance of all maintenance, including outages, while other NPPs routinely use outside contractors, particularly for outage support. Those NPPs which make use of such contractors need to specify in their training policies how the quality of outside contractor personnel work will be ensured, for example by auditing the qualifications of these personnel. Also, the training policy should be adapted to the characteristics and quality of the national systems for theoretical and practical education.

6

The scope of the training policy should apply to all staff who will work at or visit the NPP. It should briefly state for which training programmes SAT will be used. For example, does the SAT methodology apply to subcontractor or supplier personnel? If so, to what extent? How does the policy address training provided by outside contractors and technical schools?

2.3.2. Responsibilities for training

The responsibilities for providing training to attain and to maintain NPP personnel competence are assigned to a variety of groups (within and outside the plant). Many operating organizations have established training organizations to which some of these responsibilities are assigned. One of the reasons why operating organizations establish training organizations is that training requires specialized personnel. SAT evaluation provides an effective mechanism for determining that responsibilities for training are being met.

It is necessary for the training policy to define the responsibilities and authorities of the plant manager and those assigned by him to the plant department managers and to the plant training manager for all aspects of the training and qualification of NPP personnel. The division of responsibilities and authorities must emphasize clarity and appropriateness.

It is important to note that, depending on the specific organizational arrangement for training in an individual country, various tasks can be assigned not only to plant departments but also to a central training organization run by the operating organization. In some instances, training organizations external to the operating organization may be used. Whatever organizational arrangement exists for training, the final responsibility for personnel competence lies with the plant manager. (For further information, see IAEA Safety Series SS 50-SG-01, Rev. 1 on Staffing of Nuclear Power Plants and the Recruitment, Training and Authorization of Operating Personnel).

Plant manager responsibilities

- Define and assign responsibilities and authorities of all plant organizational units which report directly to the plant manager, including responsibilities for training and qualification of NPP personnel;
- Meet relevant regulatory and other requirements;
- Establish appropriate qualification requirements and standards of performance for all NPP jobs;
- Analyse training needs and develop overall training programmes;
- Understand the principles and good practices of training system development and implementation;
- Monitor, evaluate and control performance of all plant activities including those related to training and qualification;

- Recruitment, retention and career development of NPP personnel;
- Provide or arrange for, together with the operating organization, the necessary resources and staff to implement training policy and programmes, including the adequate training and compensation of trainers;
- Create a mechanism to involve qualified NPP personnel in training activities;
- Maintain personnel competence, e.g. through continuing training.

Plant manager responsibilities typically assigned to plant department managers

- Define job specific training needs;
- Determine which individuals should participate in training modules;
- Provide subject matter expert (SME) support for the analysis, design, and development of training for NPP personnel;
- Approve the content and scheduling of all training programmes for NPP personnel;
- Provide on the job training (OJT) for their personnel based on approved training plans;
- Ensure that their personnel are provided all training needed for their job assignments;
- Assist in the implementation of training as SMEs and OJT instructors;
- Perform in-plant training;
- Make final decision on the qualification of their personnel considering the training organization's assessments;
- Make job assignments based upon successful completion of required training and attainment of the required qualifications;
- Monitor the performance of training programmes;
- Perform regular competence checks;
- Identify emerging training needs for their personnel.

Plant manager responsibilities typically assigned to the plant training manager[1]

- Co-ordinate all training for NPP personnel, including that provided by external sources;
- Lead the analysis, design and development of all training for NPP personnel including OJT;
- Procure and maintain all training tools, equipment, materials, including simulators and mock-ups;
- Provide a programme for training and qualification of all instructors in technical and teaching abilities, including those who provide training in the plant;

---

[1] Some tasks of the plant training manager may be assigned to external training organizations.

- Provide QA of training from internal and external sources;
- Assess trainees;
- Lead overall training evaluation and feedback process, with continual support from and interaction with plant departments for which training is provided;
- Provide periodic reports to the plant manager and plant department managers on the results of evaluation of training programmes;
- Maintain records on the training and qualification of all NPP personnel, contractors, and non-plant staff which have functions to perform at the plant.

2.3.3. Monitoring, evaluation and control of training programmes

The training policy needs to include the requirement to monitor, evaluate, control and report on training programme performance/quality and to identify organizational responsibilities for this. This is a necessary but not sufficient condition for the effective monitoring of training programmes. The plant manager and plant department managers need to make it clear to their personnel through their actions that they consider the success of the training programmes to be their responsibility, even though much of the training is provided by the training organization. These actions can take a variety of forms, including, for example:

- Observe regularly the conduct of training (e.g. operation department managers observing the conduct of simulator training and supporting the feedback provided by simulator instructors);
- Review routinely the evaluation outputs with subordinates during staff meetings;
- Establish joint NPP/training organization groups to review training needs;
- Rotate personnel on a regular basis between plant departments and full time instructor positions.

SAT is an ideal management tool for monitoring and controlling the quality of training and other human performance activities, because inherent in the SAT process is continual evaluation of the training programmes as well as assessment of the performance of the trainees and job incumbents.

The cost of training is especially high in the nuclear industry. SAT provides the means for plant management to monitor the investment in training and to determine whether it is adequate or excessive. The challenge for management is to implement an efficient system for continuous evaluation of training. As a part of this system, plant management should determine the relevant indicators to measure the effectiveness, efficiency and impact of training provided. These plant specific indicators should be based upon the goals and scope of the training programmes.

2.4. TRAINING POLICY AND IMPLEMENTING PROCEDURES

It is essential for training policy to be known, understood and supported by all persons concerned. It is sometimes beneficial to have plant department managers and the plant training manager take part in developing the training policy and implementing procedures as a way of facilitating their acceptance of the policy.

Procedures for plant and training organizations concerning the development, implementation and evaluation of training programmes must be governed by, and aim at achieving, the goals of the training policy. These procedures then serve as an agreement between the plant organization and the training organization and define the training that must be provided, and its quality. SAT provides a mechanism to elaborate this agreement in a way that is consistently and clearly defined, based upon job specific training needs.

The overall NPP training policy goals and scope should determine the training requirements. It is sufficient to define a limited number of important goals.

The following is an example of a goal, a related requirement and its objectives:

Goal: "To operate the plant in a safe and efficient manner".

On the basis of such a goal, the following is an example of a related requirement:

"To train and qualify all NPP personnel on the safety aspects of their jobs before they are allowed to work without direct supervision."

To meet this requirement, the NPP might have an implementing procedure containing the following objectives:

To ensure that all necessary job related competencies are included in training programmes:

- Revise existing training programmes so that they are based on SAT.
- Incorporate into training, through the use of SAT, all safety related considerations.
- SAT analysis will include identification of these safety considerations; SAT design and development will include revision of training materials to include these safety considerations.
- These revisions are to be completed for high priority jobs in two years, and for all jobs in three years.

2.5. TRAINING AND SAFETY

It is important that the training and safety policies be co-ordinated. Training is an ideal way to promote safety culture and should therefore be fully encouraged and supported by plant management. Safety culture is a combination of attitudes on the priority of safety, together with KSAs about appropriate safety practices. The principal contributions which can be provided by training to the implementation and enhancement of safety culture are:

- Training programmes to explain the general attributes of safety culture;
- Job specific training to improve KSAs related to safety practices.

While general training programmes are useful, experience has shown that job specific training programmes can make an even more important contribution to safety culture.

Important for safety culture is knowledge about:

- Job specific safety issues such as use of appropriate safety equipment;
- Risks associated with task performance;
- Non-technical aspects of the job, such as use of proper work control methods.

These safety issues can be identified through SAT based analysis of training needs and can then be included in an integrated manner in job specific training programmes. This transforms safety culture from an esoteric concept to concrete actions that are integral to job performance. As indicated earlier, the appropriate attitude toward attaining, maintaining and enhancing safety is also necessary. Training on job specific safety aspects will only be successful if management reinforces safety culture through requiring its implementation as a routine part of job performance.

2.6. TRAINING POLICY AND HUMAN RESOURCES POLICY

To be most effective, the training policy needs to be consistent with the human resources policy (in some organizations, training is part of the human resources policy). The human resources policy addresses areas such as recruitment and selection, career planning and development, and retention of personnel.

A gap between the competencies required for adequate job performance and the actual performance of job incumbents can arise owing to:

- Changes in the jobs;
- Loss of training opportunities that previously existed such as plant commissioning;
- Loss of personnel through retirement.

Identifying and measuring this gap, which can be done using SAT, is useful for anticipating future personnel needs in human resources policy.

Therefore, training policy and human resources policy must be co-ordinated to anticipate change and future personnel needs (Fig. 2.1).

2.6.1. Broadening of training content

Constant striving to improve production efficiency, safety and reliability (and thus quality) has led to an increasing emphasis on training for human factors in areas such as communication, teamwork, reliability, man–machine interfaces, management/supervision, and analytical methods. This emphasis on human factors has led to a need for greater integration of training and human resource management activities.

Growing recognition of, and demands for acquiring, higher level cognitive abilities have occurred owing to job complexity and rapid technological advances, where such abilities cover not only the use of new equipment but also the understanding of basic concepts necessary to use the technology effectively on the job. Sometimes, the adapting of resources to meet emerging needs may lead to the special qualification of a small number of personnel, either because the task is rarely performed or because it calls for special KSAs obtained through training which is highly specific and/or expensive.

2.6.2. Selection and recruitment

Training and qualification of NPP personnel is a continuous process with high costs. Thus, selection, recruitment and training policies must be established with a view towards long term return on investment and on the postulate of job stability within the operating organization, that is, that future performance will largely be achieved with today's people. Therefore, selection, recruitment and training must be co-ordinated to ensure that, collectively, NPP personnel have the skills needed to attain the organization's goals and that they are capable of adapting to new technologies and new requirements.

2.6.3. Motivation and career development

It is well known that training is not effective unless trainees are motivated to learn. Job stability is an asset that the operating organization must use to find the right balance between internal promotion and external recruitment so as to sustain professional motivation. Thus, there are two inseparable, complementary components in motivating NPP personnel:

- Providing these personnel with career development prospects;
- Ensuring a positive connection between individual aspirations and the needs of the operating organization/NPP.

The career path should take into account the individual's professional evolution in the job. The need and aim to give selected plant staff more responsibility, and the need to adapt to the faster evolution of jobs require the development of meaningful career paths based on the concept of increased competencies needed for new or additional tasks or duties. SAT provides supervisors with valuable information to facilitate the definition of such tasks and duties before they are assigned to staff (i.e. through job descriptions). The SAT process also facilitates the joint determination, by supervisors and their staff, of the training that staff should receive to assist in achieving their career development goals.

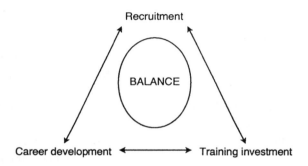

FIG. 2.1. Balance among management responsibilities for human resources development.

2.7. OPERATING ORGANIZATION INTERFACE WITH THE REGULATOR

One of the regulator's responsibilities is to ensure that NPP personnel who perform tasks important to safety are qualified to perform these tasks.

One of the principal objectives of NPP personnel training and qualification is to meet relevant regulatory requirements. Among the most common regulatory requirements with respect to NPP personnel are those requiring licensing/authorization of control room operators and their supervisors. Other common regulatory requirements include training and qualification regarding safety related topics such as radiation protection and industrial safety.

SAT provides a mechanism for the operating organization to demonstrate to the regulator and, if required, to the public that personnel are competent. SAT is able to do this because it includes analysis of the job to identify needed competencies, training programmes based on achieving these competencies, and evaluation to ensure and demonstrate that these competencies have been achieved, as well as feedback from plant operation that identifies additional competencies that are needed.

13

The regulator needs to make independent determinations that NPP personnel are qualified to perform their assigned tasks. In making these determinations, it is very valuable if both the regulator and the NPP can agree upon the standard to which job performance and training programmes are to be evaluated. Where the regulator has accepted SAT as the appropriate approach for training NPP personnel, and this is the case in many countries with nuclear power programmes, the regulator will in general also accept the SAT methodology as a basis for its own evaluation of training programmes.

It is important for the NPP and training organizations to open the entire training process to the representatives of the regulator. These regulatory representatives should be encouraged to observe all aspects of training programme development and implementation. They should also be encouraged to share with plant management their questions and concerns about what they observe. The NPP can use these observations as inputs to the overall training programme evaluation process and can demonstrate to the regulator that its observations and concerns were appropriately taken into account.

Regulators in many countries already require or strongly recommend that SAT be used for NPP personnel training. In such cases of SAT based training, regulators have shifted their focus from prescribing detailed curricula in particular areas to an independent evaluation of the training identified as required and provided by the NPP.

Also, in those countries where SAT based training has been endorsed by the regulator, licensing examinations for selected positions, such as control room operators and shift supervisors, should be based on the operating organization's or NPP's job analyses and should be consistent with the related training objectives and the associated training materials.

3. THE ROLE OF TRAINING ORGANIZATIONS AND THE ORGANIZATION OF TRAINING

This section is primarily addressed to training organization managers and specialists and also to plant department managers and supervisors who interface with training organizations.

3.1. ORGANIZATION OF TRAINING

The operating organization must define all responsibilities for the training of NPP personnel, which should be included in the training policy document and in the written procedures for SAT. Various organizational arrangements for training have been used by different operating organizations.

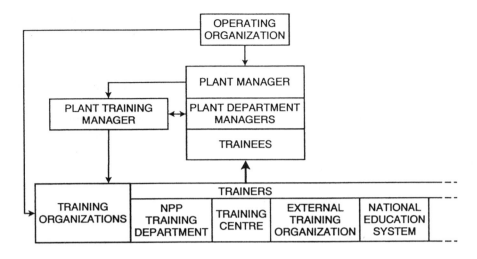

FIG. 3.1. Typical organizational arrangements for the training of NPP personnel.

The plant manager is ultimately responsible for ensuring that all the personnel involved in safety related work are competent. Therefore, the plant manager is responsible for ensuring that the personnel are adequately trained.

The plant manager will assign responsibility for certain aspects of the training process to other persons and/or organizations. Sometimes, nearly the whole training process is implemented by NPP staff and sometimes most of it is implemented by a central training organization run by the operating organization or by external organizations. Figure 3.1 presents a typical organizational arrangement for NPP personnel training.

3.2. INTERFACES BETWEEN PLANT MANAGER AND TRAINING ORGANIZATIONS

For some NPPs, training organizations report directly to the plant manager. The plant training manager and plant department managers are peers. In this case, the plant manager is responsible for resolving conflicts between the potentially competing priorities of the training organizations and plant departments. For example, there may be times when, owing to their departments' workloads, plant department managers may not feel they can release their personnel either for receiving or for conducting scheduled training. If plant departments and the plant training manager cannot resolve such issues, the plant manager must do so.

15

For other NPPs, the training organizations do not report to the plant manager. They may be in entirely different operating organization units that only come together at the highest levels of the operating organization. In this case, there is the same need for communication and conflict resolution as described above, but the mechanisms for resolving conflicts will require the involvement of higher level management of the operating organization.

The plant training managers should assist plant manager(s) in carrying out their responsibilities for establishing and disseminating policies and procedures concerning NPP personnel training and qualification. These policies and procedures must be plant documents and not training organization documents. This makes it clear to plant department managers that these policies and procedures apply to their departments and that the procedures have the full support of the plant manager.

The plant manager often assigns to training organizations the task of establishing a training programme evaluation process, and of collecting the information needed to implement this process. Assignment of responsibilities and duties between the training organizations and the plant in the evaluation process should be clearly stated, on the basis of training needs identification and QA procedures. It is important that the results of the training programme evaluation process be provided to the plant manager in a clear and concise manner, and that the information be provided in a format that encourages appropriate actions by the plant manager and plant department managers.

Also, during outages, some plants will utilize outside contractor personnel to perform maintenance work. The plant training department, together with other plant departments for which the specific work is to be performed, will review the qualifications of contractor personnel and determine if any training has to be provided.

It is necessary to have sufficient information flow from the NPP to the training organizations, to keep training programmes up to date so that they can meet plant training needs. Such information includes:

- Notification of plant events
- Changes in procedures
- Experience feedback
- Equipment modifications
- Modification of NPP organization.

3.3. INTERFACES BETWEEN PLANT DEPARTMENTS AND TRAINING ORGANIZATIONS

Training organizations should understand that the only reason for their existence is to provide a service to plant departments. Therefore, they must be responsive to the needs of the NPP. The relevant individuals in plant departments and training organizations should establish communication mechanisms that ensure they maintain close contact and co-operation. For example, plant department managers should have their subject matter experts review and approve the technical content of relevant training materials. The scheduling of training programmes should be done on a co-operative basis with the NPP and not unilaterally by training organizations.

It is extremely important that instructors keep up their technical knowledge by regular participation in the work at the plant and, as a result, maintain their credibility with trainees and plant personnel. At some plants, during outages, all training centre training is suspended and instructors are integrated into the appropriate plant departments to assist with the outage. This represents a good practice as it provides assistance to the NPP while providing continuing OJT for instructors and maintaining contacts.

On the job training is an area where effective interfaces between plant departments and training organizations are particularly needed. Typically, NPP personnel conduct OJT and OJT assessments, while the training organization:

- Prepares OJT materials (with support from the relevant plant departments);
- Trains the OJT instructors/assessors in teaching/assessment techniques;
- Maintains OJT records.

3.4. INTERFACES AMONG ORGANIZATIONS AND PERSONNEL WITH TRAINING RESPONSIBILITIES

For many NPPs, there is more than one organization to which responsibilities have been assigned for providing NPP personnel training. Plant policy or procedures need to define clearly the responsibilities and interfaces among those organizations/ personnel that perform the various types of training.

There is almost always a plant training manager who reports either directly to the plant manager or to another manager in the operating organization or NPP. The following training activities are usually assigned to organizations and personnel who report to the plant training manager:

- Job specific OJT;
- Classroom/laboratory training on general safety topics such as radiation protection, industrial safety, labour laws, QA and fire protection;
- Job specific theoretical training;
- Job specific simulator training (e.g. operator training on a full scope control room simulator);
- Job specific laboratory/workshop training (e.g. instrumentation and control laboratories);
- Training on vendor specific equipment (e.g. overhaul of electrical generators).

Job specific OJT will obviously be conducted in the plant, while for many NPPs the other training tasks are performed by one or more training centres, either near the plant or at some regional location.

Some operating organizations use external training organizations to provide specific training modules or to augment training organization staffs. These external training organizations often report directly to the plant training manager or his designate. External training organizations should be subject to the same standards and QA requirements as NPP/operating organization personnel involved in providing training.

4. SAT METHODOLOGY OVERVIEW

The purpose of Sections 4 to 9 is to provide guidance in the use of SAT methodology for the training of NPP personnel and a description of the activities, input and output of each phase of SAT. The experience of many countries and NPPs in the use of SAT has been taken into account in developing this guidance.

SAT Definition

> **An approach that provides a logical progression from the identification of the competencies required to perform a job to the development and implementation of training to achieve these competencies, and subsequent evaluation of this training.**

SAT is a methodology which applies QA to training and thus assures NPP personnel competence. The use of SAT offers significant advantages over more conventional, curricula driven training in terms of consistency, efficiency and management control. With a systematic approach to training, the competence requirements for all jobs in an NPP can be established and met. Furthermore, with SAT based training, it can be demonstrated that all required competencies have been attained.

Without SAT, there is the risk that important elements of training will be omitted, which would adversely affect the safety and reliability of the plant. There is also the potential that programmes will be too extensive for the needs of the job, with the consequent cost implications and loss of trainee motivation. Furthermore, the increased control and accountability features of the SAT process provide management as well as the regulator with the means of applying standard QA procedures and processes at any stage of the training process. The regulator may still require a certain number of examinations to license individuals in some specific positions. However, the requirement for the training process to conform with the plant QA programme provides management and the regulator with far greater confidence in the qualifications

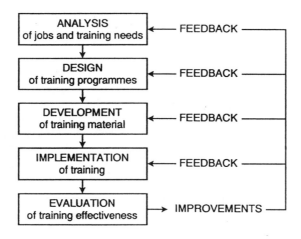

FIG. 4.1. Overview of SAT process.

and competence of personnel than that provided by a purely examination driven assessment.

An overview of the SAT process is given in Fig. 4.1.

SAT consists of five interrelated phases, which are:

ANALYSIS (See Section 5)

This phase comprises the identification of training needs and of the competencies required to perform a particular job.

DESIGN (See Section 6)

In this phase, competencies are converted into training objectives. These objectives are organized into a training plan.

DEVELOPMENT (See Section 7)

This phase comprises preparation of all training materials so that the training objectives can be achieved.

IMPLEMENTATION (See Section 8)

In this phase, training is conducted by using the training materials developed.

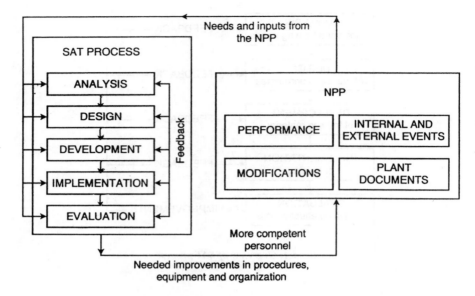

FIG. 4.2. *Relationship between SAT process and NPP.*

EVALUATION (See Section 9)

During this phase, all aspects of training programmes are evaluated on the basis of the data collected during each of the other phases. This is followed by suitable feedback leading to training programme and plant improvements.

Experience has shown that implementing procedures are needed for each of the SAT phases so that the process is implemented in such a way as to ensure quality and consistency. These procedures must specify in detail the steps to be taken to carry out the phase and to identify the responsibilities and qualifications of personnel performing the work.

It is absolutely essential for instructors to have both technical and teaching competence.

Figure 4.2 shows how the SAT process is related to NPP operation.

To introduce SAT, the main inputs and prerequisites are:

- Firstly, plant management's recognition of the need for establishing, updating and/or improving NPP personnel training programmes;
- Secondly, plant organization and job descriptions;
- Thirdly, plant and operating and maintenance documentation, for example, system descriptions, operating instructions, emergency operating procedures, inspection manuals (as well as job descriptions and responsibilities for each job position).

The better the plant and operations documentation is, the more easily the development and implementation of SAT based training can be carried out.

In the case of an NPP in the planning stage, documentation from a reference plant (if there is one) or from a plant of similar design should be obtained.

For the development of training programmes, information is needed on a continual basis from:

- Plant documents
- NPP performance indicators
- Industry operational experience
- Equipment and procedure modifications.

Evaluation of training programmes will often identify needed improvements in plant procedures, equipment and organization. The overall goal of both the SAT process and the NPP is personnel with the necessary competence to operate and maintain the NPP. This relationship between SAT and the NPP is applicable to both new and existing plants.

5. ANALYSIS

5.1. INTRODUCTION

The purpose of this phase is to identify those jobs and their related tasks and competencies for which training is required. Competencies are defined to be groups of knowledge, skills and/or attitudes (KSAs) needed to perform a particular job.

Figure 5.1 shows the inputs and outputs for the SAT analysis phase. For this phase, the importance of inputs from the plant needs to be emphasized. Both the quality and the relevance of training programmes are highly dependent on these inputs.

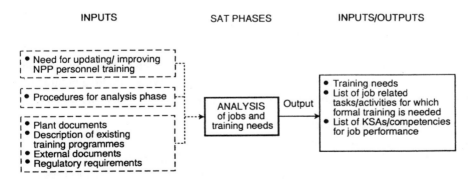

FIG. 5.1. Inputs to and outputs from the analysis phase.

21

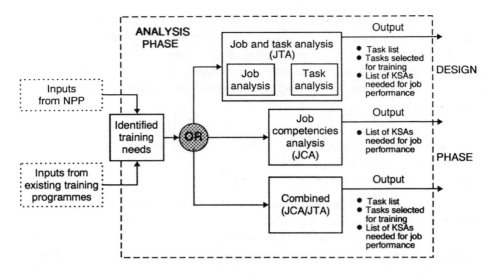

FIG. 5.2. Overview of the analysis phase.

5.2. TYPES OF ANALYSIS

The following sections describe the types of analysis used by NPPs, and lessons learned in applying the various types of analysis. Figure 5.2 shows the relationships between different types of analysis that may be performed during this phase. The most important point to note with respect to this figure is that regardless of what type of analysis is selected for use, each provides very similar outputs, including the KSAs needed for job performance. These KSAs provide the basis for the training objectives that are developed during the design phase.

5.3. IDENTIFYING TRAINING NEEDS

The first step in the analysis phase is to identify training needs. This is a prerequisite for decisions on the need for developing or improving a training programme. Identifying training needs begins with information collection, which should include:

- Performance of job incumbents;
- Job performance deficiencies;
- Changes due to lessons learned from operational experience;
- Changes in plant systems, documents (e.g. procedures, technical specifications) and regulatory requirements;

- Information about the content of existing training programmes and the qualifications of personnel;
- Regulatory requirements.

If there is no training programme in place, such information may be obtained from reference plants, design documentation and safety analysis reports.

Training needs can arise because of new requirements on the organizational units to which jobs belong. Identifying the training needs for a particular job must therefore be preceded by a careful review of new tasks at the organizational level.

To identify training needs, deficiencies in performance are examined and appropriate solutions identified. Changes or additions to training programmes may or may not be appropriate solutions. Other possible solutions to performance problems include:

- Improved procedures
- Equipment modifications
- Improved safety
- Improved supervision.

Only if training needs can be identified does the process continue to the subsequent steps of the analysis phase.

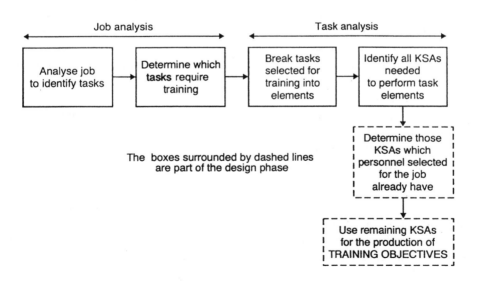

FIG. 5.3. Overview of job and task analysis steps.

5.4. JOB AND TASK ANALYSIS (JTA)

In the past, the analysis phase of SAT was synonymous with job and task analysis. Figure 5.3 is an overview of the steps of job analysis and task analysis. KSAs for which training is to be provided (remaining KSAs) are obtained from the difference between all KSAs needed for job competence and those which the selected personnel already have.

5.4.1. Job analysis

Job analysis is a process to produce a list of tasks to be addressed by the training programme for a specific job. Tasks are defined work sequences within a job, with identifiable start and end points (e.g. calibrate a pressure detector). Thus, the task list clearly and accurately defines a particular job. The description of a task should include the corresponding performance standard and conditions; this permits subsequent development of training objectives.

Documents related to job performance are one of the necessary inputs for job analysis and typically include:

- Plant safety analysis reports;
- Plant design safety guidelines;
- Operating rules/technical specifications;
- Plant design information pertinent to each job to be performed (for example, plant logic diagrams, plant item descriptions);
- Operational experience reports/analyses;
- Normal and abnormal operating instructions, and emergency operating procedures;
- Plant maintenance instructions;
- Detailed list of the activities of particular plant staff (e.g. operating, maintenance, training, management/supervision personnel);
- Job descriptions for each job position;
- Job analyses completed for related jobs or similar plants;
- Regulatory requirements.

It is important to review and adapt the data obtained from other plants to ensure its applicability. If not all tasks for a job are included in documentation, then surveys or interviews with job incumbents and their supervisors will be needed to complete the task list. In the case of a plant in the planning stage, documentation from the reference plant (if there is one), or from plants of similar design, should be obtained.

After the tasks have been identified, those that need to be included in the initial training programme are selected. Generally, tasks selected for initial training are:

24

- Important for safe and reliable plant operation;
- Of a level of difficulty/complexity requiring formal training.

From these tasks, those for which competence is not expected to be maintained through working on the job should be included in the continuing training programme. Examples of such tasks are infrequently performed tasks such as those related to in-service inspection or to response to plant emergencies.

Supervisors should review the results of the job analysis. The review should confirm that task lists include all tasks necessary for safe and reliable plant operations, and that tasks selected for initial and continuing training are appropriate.

5.4.2. Task analysis

As shown in Fig. 5.3., task analysis involves first dividing tasks into their elements (steps) and then determining the KSAs needed to perform each element. Results of task analysis provide data from which performance standards and training objectives are produced during the design phase. Task analysis also includes identification of required work attitudes such as safety awareness (operational and industrial safety) and fitness for duty.

The data necessary to perform task analysis are extracted from plant documents or from other sources (interviews with job incumbents and others, existing training materials, feedback, experience, data on plant modifications, etc.). Task analysis should be conducted by experienced and knowledgeable persons using standardized methods. The methods used by NPPs for the conduct of task analysis have included:

- Interviews (both individual and group interviews);
- Table top analyses using expert groups;
- Review of existing analyses;
- Review of procedures.

5.4.3. Lessons learned concerning JTA

5.4.3.1. Resource demands/information overload

Many NPPs have found that their JTA required a disproportionate demand on human, financial resources and time and went into too much detail. As a result, these NPPs produced such a large amount of data that they were unable effectively to manage the information or to use it for training design and development. Three lessons were learned from this experience:

- Do not identify tasks at too low a level, and thus generate a large number of tasks, task elements, and associated KSAs.

Job specific KSA categories

Components	Systems	Basic technology	Working methods	Human factors
KSAs associated with NPP components, e.g.	KSAs associated with NPP systems, e.g.	KSAs associated with NPP theory/technology, e.g.	KSAs associated with NPP procedures to perform work, e.g.	KSAs associated with human attributes necessary to perform work, e.g.
Pumps • functions • characteristics • locations • centrifugal • etc. **Heat exchangers** • functions • locations • direct contact • plate • tube • etc.	**Reactor coolant** • functions • components • design limits • alarms etc. **Condensate** • components • flow path • etc.	**Reactor theory** • neutron • kinetics • heat transfer • etc. **Electrical theory** • machines • batteries • Kirchoff • etc.	**Technical specifications** • limiting conditioning of operation • etc. **Procedures** • operating • maintenance • communication • etc.	**Communication** • written • oral • etc. **Teamwork** • roles • leadership • etc. **Management** • decision making • etc.

FIG. 5.4. Job specific KSA categories.

- Organize JTA data using database management software, to be able to maintain and update the information.

Use a structure to organize JTA data in a manner useful for training design and development. Figure 5.4 shows an example of such a structure that would be suitable for plant operating personnel. Such a structure provides a way of dealing effectively with the situation that occurs often in JTA, where KSAs are common to several tasks. Through this structure, KSAs need to be entered only once into a database and can then be referenced to all the tasks to which they apply.

5.4.3.2. Analysing higher level cognitive and human factors competencies

Tasks can range from simple (e.g. dismantling a pump) to complex (e.g. tasks involving a search for defects, or diagnosing abnormal and emergency operational conditions). The analysis of routine tasks with prescribed sequential steps is simple and straightforward Task analysis in such cases identifies task elements, their sequences and corresponding KSAs and performance standards. The difficulty lies in performing analysis for complex, non-repetitive tasks and particularly in determining performance standards for such tasks. Determining the competence requirements for jobs which involve this higher level cognitive competencies (e.g. control room operators, managerial positions, safety analysts) must use structured expert judgement as part of the analysis. Of particular importance for such analysis are job tasks/activities for which step by step procedures have not been, or cannot be, developed.

Some JTAs have primarily focused on the technical aspects of NPP jobs. As a result, they did not necessarily identify human factors competencies in areas such as communication, teamwork, management and supervision, and man–machine interface. Section 5.8 provides more information on these human factors competencies.

5.4.3.3. Use of JTAs from other NPPs

For certain NPP positions JTAs have already been performed by such bodies as the US Institute of Nuclear Power Operations and the United States Nuclear Regulatory Commission. They have been put into a format such that they would be useful to those in other organizations who may wish to develop training programmes for certain NPP positions. In cases where jobs at one NPP are quite similar to those at another NPP which has already completed a JTA, the JTA data from the latter plant can be reviewed and revised as needed, rather than performing a complete JTA. Difficulties have arisen in applying JTA data from one NPP to another which has a different organizational structure, different staffing arrangements or different technologies.

Generic JTAs have been performed for the following positions:

- Control room operator
- Field operator
- Instrumentation and control technician
- Electrical maintenance technician
- Mechanical maintenance technician
- Radiological protection technician
- Chemistry technician
- Quality control technician
- Instructor.

5.5. JOB COMPETENCIES ANALYSIS (JCA)

On the basis of the lessons learned from the use of JTA by NPPs, some NPPs have used alternative types of analysis. One of these may be described as job competencies analysis (JCA). Competencies are groups of related KSAs needed to perform a particular job. For example, a competency for a reactor operator might be knowledge of reactor cooling flowpaths during all modes of operation. One of the KSAs related

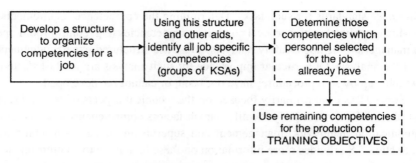

Boxes surrounded by dashed lines are part of the design phase.
However, for this type of analysis, an expert group usually carries out
the whole process in an integrated manner.

FIG. 5.5. Summary of job competencies analysis.

to this competency would be knowledge of the reactor cooling flowpath at 100%
power. Figure 5.5 summarizes the JCA process.

JCA uses a structured process to gather information on the collective experience, knowledge and judgement of a group of experts, to identify all the competencies needed for a particular job.

For JCA, it is usual that an expert group conducts a structured analysis of a particular job or a set of related jobs. A procedure is approved in advance in order to maintain the necessary logical, systematic and documented approach during the identification of competencies.

The group is chosen so as to bring together all necessary expertise related to the job being considered. The expertise required of the expert group needed for JCA may be divided into the following categories:

Technical

- Plant design safety guidelines;
- Job requirements;
- Plant specific design and operation;
- Methods used in the performance of tasks and constraints under which they are performed;
- Operational experience feedback;
- Training needs resulting from procedure changes or plant modifications.

28

- Communication, leadership and other human factors KSAs required of the job incumbent (see Section 5.8);
- Range of experience and education of the potential trainees;
- Legal and other mandatory requirements of the job incumbent;
- QA system at the plant;
- Safety culture;
- Management systems and plant organization;
- Use of procedures for operations, maintenance and other activities.

Training

- Knowledge of each phase of SAT, its inputs, outputs and purposes;
- Knowledge of the details of existing training programmes.

This expert group would typically include the following:

- Job incumbent(s);
- Instructor(s)/training developer(s);
- Job incumbent(s)' supervisor/manager;
- A chairman/facilitator;
- For some jobs, representative(s) of educational/training organizations.

The expert group should be large enough to provide the breadth of expertise needed while being small enough to be of a workable size. Figure 5.5 shows that the output of the JCA is used to produce training objectives. The responsibilities of the expert group usually include the production of training objectives, thus combining parts of the analysis and design phases of SAT.

5.5.1. Lessons learned concerning JCA

Experience has shown that both the correct constitution of the expert groups and a structured method of controlling the groups' work are necessary to ensure that the output of the JCA is systematically derived. An important aspect of JCA is that it makes systematic use of collective experience so that the derived competencies list is accurate and complete.

Some operating organizations have established JCA expert groups which have the additional responsibility for evaluation of the overall training process. This provides a means for continuous evaluation of training programmes, as well as helping to ensure that those improvements identified through evaluation are properly implemented.

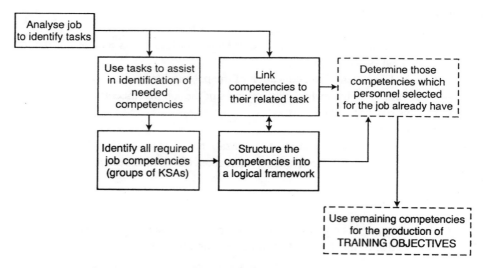

Boxes surrounded by dashed lines are part of the design phase

FIG. 5.6. Example of a combined JTA and JCA.

5.6. COMBINED JTA AND JCA

As SAT analysis methods have evolved, some NPPs have found it beneficial to combine JTA and JCA. Figure 5.6 shows an example of one way in which JTA and JCA have been combined. In this example, a job analysis is first conducted to identify tasks. Then, the tasks are used to help in identifying competencies needed for the job. The competencies are each linked to one or more tasks to assist in the production of training objectives. It can be seen that the example KSA structure shown in Fig. 5.4 could be used equally well to support JTA, JCA, or this combined JTA/JCA method.

5.7. SELECTION OF TYPE(S) OF ANALYSIS

It is clear from the preceding sections that there is no one type of analysis that would be appropriate to every situation and every NPP. Each NPP must determine the types of analysis appropriate for its needs. Collaboration between those responsible for personnel training and those responsible for NPP operation should lead to the selection of the most appropriate method for a particular NPP.

In making the selection the following questions should typically be taken into account:

- Are there performance deficiencies in job incumbents that suggest the need for significant training development?
- Can a thorough analysis of all tasks lead to identification of weaknesses in areas other than training? Examples include procedures, man–machine interfaces and diagnostic aids.
- Is it known in advance that certain tasks will require higher level cognitive abilities and human factors competencies?
- Are detailed, step by step procedures available for the tasks being analysed?
- Does a training programme already exist for the particular job under consideration?
- What resources, in terms of personnel, money and time, can be allocated?
- How soon must significant training or training improvements be implemented?
- How readily can the analysis data be updated by the type of analysis under consideration?
- How readily can training materials be linked to plant specific tasks?
- Does the type of analysis encourage plant staff involvement in, and commitment to, their training programmes?
- Is it planned that the analysis data will be used by other NPPs?

5.8. HUMAN FACTORS COMPETENCIES FOR NPP PERSONNEL

Experience has shown that technical competencies related to the NPP and its processes are not sufficient to ensure the competence of NPP personnel and performance according to established international standards. Experience has also shown that, as was mentioned in Section 5.4.3.2, these human factors competencies have not always been fully identified, particularly for more complex tasks. For this reason, examples of these competencies are presented below, organized by functional category:

Communication

- Interface with plant staff within the NPP;
- Interface with outside agencies or groups;
- Inform management of plant conditions;
- Conduct group presentations or meetings;
- Write operational reports, procedures and other documents;
- Report problems and identifying solutions.

Team building and teamwork

- Promote teamwork and apply team skills;
- Demonstrate respect for individuals;
- Request needed assistance and guidance.

Management and supervision

- Enforce standards of performance;
- Use coaching and teaching methods with subordinates and trainees;
- Demonstrate initiative and perseverance;
- Apply informed judgement;
- Motivate subordinates;
- Supervise subordinates;
- Counsel subordinates;
- Conduct personnel performance appraisals;
- Provide constructive feedback;
- Apply assertiveness skills;
- Plan and organize work.

Leadership

- Exhibit composure during abnormal/emergency events;
- Intervene to restore a colleague's composure;
- Advocate an attitude of conservatism for reactor safety;
- Promote a constructive, questioning attitude;
- Exhibit a positive, optimistic attitude;
- Establish an environment which encourages the reporting of problems to supervisors.

Analytical methods

- Apply problem solving fundamentals;
- Establish priorities;
- Recognize risks and consequences;
- Recognize aberrant behaviour of colleagues and subordinates.

Man–machine interface

- Recognize weaknesses in procedures and other documentation;
- Recognize man–machine interface weaknesses in plant controls and displays.

6. DESIGN

6.1. INTRODUCTION

The purpose of the design phase is to convert the competencies/KSAs that were selected for training during the analysis phase into training objectives, and to sequence these training objectives into a training plan for initial and continuing training.

Figure 6.1 shows the inputs and outputs of SAT up to and including the design phase.

Figure 6.2 shows the relationships among the activities performed during the design phase. The important first step is to convert KSAs into measurable and objective training objectives. This step is interrelated with the establishment of entry level requirements for training programmes (e.g. education, experience and previous training), as this decision determines the level at which training objectives are written. At the end of this phase, all steps shown in Fig. 6.2 provide inputs to the training plan.

The training plan is made up of the following components:

- List of training objectives;
- Training settings to be used to meet those objectives;
- Schedule of training modules for both initial and continuing training;
- Identification of those training objectives that should be addressed for both initial and continuing training;
- Identification of those modules that will cover training for more than one staff group or family of jobs;
- Entry level requirements of trainees;
- Test items;
- Estimates of resources needed for development and implementation.

The plan also identifies responsibilities for programme development and implementation, including review and approval of training materials. For most jobs, the responsibilities for training programme implementation will be divided between training organization(s) staff and plant personnel.

6.2. TRAINING OBJECTIVES

Training objectives are statements of what trainees will be able to do upon completion of a particular part of a training programme, to what standards and under what conditions. Training objectives must always have the following components:

- **Subject**   (always the trainee)
- **Verb**   (a measurable, action type verb)

33

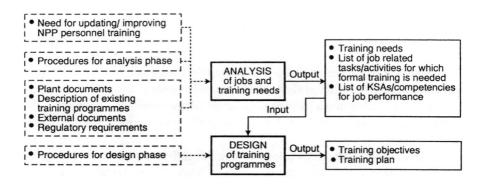

INPUTS   SAT PHASES   INPUTS/OUTPUTS

- Need for updating/ improving NPP personnel training

- Procedures for analysis phase

- Plant documents
- Description of existing training programmes
- External documents
- Regulatory requirements

ANALYSIS of jobs and training needs

Output

- Training needs
- List of job related tasks/activities for which formal training is needed
- List of KSAs/competencies for job performance

Input

- Procedures for design phase

DESIGN of training programmes

Output

- Training objectives
- Training plan

FIG. 6.1. Inputs to and outputs from the design phase.

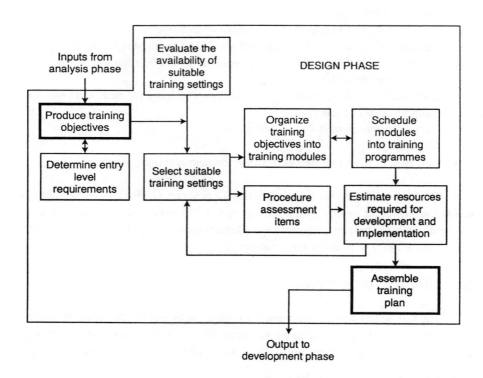

FIG. 6.2. Relationship of steps in the design phase.

34

- **Object**   (upon which the action (verb) is to be taken)
- **Conditions** (the conditions under which the action is to be undertaken)
- **Standards**   (the standards which the trainee must achieve)

Training objectives explicitly identify trainee performance standards and are, therefore, the basis for assessing trainees upon completion of training or a part thereof. They provide a direct link between the job and the training programme. Not only are training objectives important to the instructor, but they also inform trainees precisely on what is expected of them.

There are two types of training objectives: terminal and enabling.

Terminal objectives are directly related to specific tasks/competencies and reflect trainee performance requirements upon completion of a training programme. Terminal objectives are developed for each competency selected for training. The following is an example of a terminal objective:

Subject and Verb	Object	Conditions	Standard
Upon completion of the training programme, the trainee will be able to point out	each component and connection in the condensate system from the suction of the condenser extraction pump to the suction of the main feed pumps	while tracing the system in the turbine hall	identifying all components and connections with 100% accuracy, in a time of 40 minutes

Enabling objectives are training objectives that must be mastered before the terminal training objective can be accomplished.

The following is an example of an enabling objective. It could relate to a terminal objective associated with a control room operator's task to control xenon transients during reactor power changes:

Subject and Verb	Object	Conditions	Standard
At the end of the training session the control room operator trainee will be able to identify	reactor fission product poisons	in writing under examination conditions	providing the names of the two most significant regarding reactor operation

6.3. SELECTING TRAINING SETTINGS AND SCHEDULING TRAINING MODULES

The training plan for a particular training programme organizes related training objectives into lessons and related lessons into training modules. These training modules are then sequenced, in an order which supports efficient and effective learning. The training modules are each allocated to a training setting. For training NPP operating and maintenance personnel, the most commonly used training settings include the following:

- Classroom
- Simulation
- On the job training
- Laboratory or workshop
- Computer based training (CBT)
- Self-study
- Mock-up.

Alternating between on the job, classroom, simulator and other training settings has been found to be beneficial to maintain trainees' motivation. Training programme designers often place a limit on the time which should be spent in a particular setting. Trainees should not be away from the plant for too long a period of time so as not to lose competencies developed through earlier training and experience. A mixture of training settings should enhance their ability to learn. Also, not all people learn in the same way. Varying training setting provides a way to accommodate different learning styles. Some operator training programmes, for example, contain a sequence of modules that start with two weeks of classroom training, followed by OJT, followed by two weeks of simulator training.

For some jobs it may be possible to organize training modules around a group of related tasks that represent only a portion of the total job. In this way, NPP personnel can be qualified to perform useful work before completion of the full programme. This approach is most common for maintenance personnel training. For example, personnel may receive qualification to perform maintenance on plant equipment which is not contaminated before they receive their full radiological protection training.

6.3.1. Factors affecting the selection of training settings

Experience has shown that there are no universally appropriate training settings. The personnel responsible for training design, development and implementation should have a detailed knowledge of the different training settings available, as well as the strengths and limitations of each setting. They must determine the training setting that best fulfils training objectives and is compatible with the:

36

- Level and ability of trainees;
- Type of material to be learned;
- Training resources required;
- Training aids required.

Alternative training settings should also be identified, as constraints may dictate compromises, particularly when the primary selection has adverse effects on plant operation (e.g. taking plant equipment out of service for OJT).

To ensure that the most useful available training setting can be used, particular attention should be given to:

- Timely availability of plant facilities;
- On the job training scheduled to take account of access opportunities provided by the plant operating conditions including outages;
- Availability of a plant specific or other type of simulator;
- Availability of classroom facilities;
- Availability of laboratory facilities;
- Scheduling of trainees to ensure class sizes are optimized and not too large.

Selection of the training setting affects the degree of fidelity (accuracy in reproducing actual task conditions in the work environment) with which individuals can be trained to perform a given task. Selection of the training setting should consider the fidelity required for effective training. For this purpose, tasks can be divided into three categories:

6.3.1.1. Tasks requiring complete replication

Tasks in this group have two characteristics:

- They are very important for plant safety and reliability;
- They cannot be trained to required standards in any other way than by complete replication.

Examples of such tasks for control room operators are those associated with responding to abnormal or emergency conditions. Full scope replica simulators and actual plant facilities/equipment are training tools that provide complete replication for training such tasks. Similarly, for maintenance personnel, the plant or full scale mock-ups provide complete replication. Training programmes for tasks associated with the maintenance and calibration of reactor protection systems are increasingly making use of simulators that provide complete replication without jeopardizing plant operation.

6.3.1.2. Tasks requiring less than full scope replication

Selection of the most realistic training setting for all training objectives is not always necessary, because a less expensive or less time consuming setting may also allow achievement of a set of related training objectives. Tasks of this type can be trained on part task simulators or in laboratories or workshops in an environment not necessarily equivalent to the job environment.

An example of this type of task is the calibration of a transducer. The important part of the task execution is the competence to perform the calibration with the appropriate equipment. Less importance is attached to the environment(s) in which it may need to be performed.

6.3.1.3. Training objectives that can be grouped and taught independently of individual tasks

For these items, classroom or even self-study training may be selected. In many instances, this training will be preparation for training for the first two categories of tasks.

6.3.2. Classroom training

Classroom training is led by an instructor and includes the following:

- Lectures/lessons;
- Demonstrations making use of documents, drawings, models, photos, films, transparencies, etc;
- Discussions;
- Solving problems under instructor supervision;
- Exercises such as role playing.

SAT based classroom training is appropriate for the following reasons:

- Consistency in presentation and content which meets the required standards can be maintained;
- Large quantities of information can be presented in a limited amount of time;
- Large groups of trainees can simultaneously participate in the training;
- It is less expensive and easier to organize than other forms of instruction;
- It does not interfere with plant operation or depend upon plant operational status;
- Favourable training environment can be easily secured (light, temperature, comfortable environment);
- Many training tools and media can be efficiently used (overhead transparencies, slides, video, films, computer aided training, models and small mock-ups);

- Discussion with the instructor and between the trainees is facilitated;
- Assessments can be easily conducted.

In a training programme, classroom training is typically divided into modules, each having a specified duration. The modules are subdivided into units, usually referred to as lessons, whose duration is controlled to maintain trainee attention.

6.3.3. Training using simulation

For many NPPs, simulator training has only been considered for control room operators. However, many plants have extended simulator training to maintenance and other operations jobs. The importance of simulation in training programmes for NPP personnel cannot be overemphasized. This section discusses not only simulator training for control room operators but also the use of simulation training for a wide range of other NPP personnel.

6.3.3.1. Types of simulator

The types of simulator described in this section are those most commonly used by NPPs and are consistent with those mentioned in IAEA-TECDOC-685, Simulators for Training Nuclear Power Plant Personnel.

Full scope simulators

The most common example of a full scope simulator is the full scope control room simulator which usually allows for simulation of the full range of operations that can be performed from the main control room. They are usually plant referenced and replicate as many systems as possible, including communications, as well as duplicating the actual control room environment. Generic examples of such simulators exist for particular types of plant where typical conditions are represented while maintaining the dynamics of the system. Some are hardware and/or software reconfigurable. Other applications of this type of simulator include their use for I&C technician training in the maintenance and calibration of reactor protection systems. Some training objectives associated with trouble shooting, fault diagnosis on important systems or reactor protection systems can only be achieved by using full scope simulation.

Part task simulators

Part task simulators are designed for achieving particular training objectives associated with specific plant items or phenomena. They can range from providing simulation of simple system operation through to detailed fault finding on major sections of plant. As the name implies, they do not provide simulation of all aspects of a task.

Basic principles simulators

Basic principles simulators are generally associated with enabling objectives, rather than terminal objectives. They help trainees to understand the principles of a complex system or activity by presenting simplified models or equipment.

In practice, many variants of these three basic types of simulator exist. It is worth while, however, to add the additional category of multifunctional simulators, owing to their potential flexibility and cost effectiveness.

Multifunctional simulators

This type of simulator generally has the same model of plant system operation as a full scope simulator, but with simplified controls and indications. These controls and displays are generally provided through a graphical interface, representing plant system mimic diagrams. Multifunctional simulators can be used to achieve objectives which are sometimes allocated to basic principles simulators, part task simulators or full scope simulators. In the latter case, training objectives associated with the control room environment cannot be achieved.

Multifunctional simulators are a useful precursor to the plant specific, high fidelity, replica simulator, both from the viewpoint of training and of simulator development and configuration management.

The possibilities afforded by modern simulators are far reaching and can be applied to many different tasks. The final choice of a particular device depends on its effectiveness in providing training for the selected tasks, and on the cost of the simulator. Also, in recent years, the capabilities of CBT to incorporate simulation have increased the possible options for simulator training.

6.3.3.2. Components of initial training programmes for control room operators based on simulators

The most common use of simulators at NPPs is for both initial and continuing training of control room operators and shift supervisors. Simulator training for control room operators includes exercises corresponding to normal, abnormal and emergency plant operating conditions. These exercises also provide opportunities to gain valuable operating experience in those modes of operation which are rarely, if ever, encountered in practice. It is usual to divide simulator training for control room operators into a number of related modules, including:

- Normal operation;
- Abnormal operation and malfunctions;
- Emergency and accident operations;
- Control room supervisor training;
- Shift supervisor training.

There are also training lessons normally associated with classroom training that can benefit from being illustrated on a basic principles simulator capable of demonstrating plant transients in faster than real time or through CBT. An example of a training objective for control room operator training on the reactivity effects of xenon is provided below:

By the end of the training programme, the trainee control room operator will be able to:	sketch graphs of the variation of reactivity due to the variation in concentration of xenon-135, following power changes of: 100 to 0%, i.e. reactor trip 0 to 100% 50 to 100% 100 to 50% Approximate values of reactivity worth at equilibrium and peak levels should be included as well as an approximate time-scale.

There are obvious advantages over classroom training in simulating this phenomenon, particular if the demonstration can be structured in such as way as to have the trainee take appropriate actions rather than simply listening to, or watching, the instructor.

Another typical example of a training objective associated with operator training is provided below:

By the end of the training programme, the trainee control room operator will be able to:	start up the complete unit, according to the procedure, from refuelling shutdown to full power, without assistance from an instructor, in real time; given the procedure, explain the reason for each procedure step in the above, in detail to a defined standard.

If a full scope simulator is available, it would be the obvious setting in which to train this objective. However, if a full scope simulator is not available, the selection of an appropriate training setting is more problematical. The first part of the objective may be achieved by using a combination of classroom training, basic principles simulation (if available) and an extended period of OJT, during which the trainee successively has the operation demonstrated to him, performs the operation under supervision, and ultimately is assessed during supervised performance of the actual operation.

The second part of the objective could be achieved by using a multifunctional simulator. CBT might actually achieve this objective in a more efficient manner than a full scope simulator when used in combination with classroom and possibly self-study training.

At a more advanced part of training, a training objective such as that below might be included:

By the end of the training programme, the trainee control room operator will be able to:	diagnose and mitigate the consequences of any design basis accident, followed by the necessary actions, according to the procedure, with assistance from a colleague reading the step by step instructions;
	explain the reason for each procedure step in the above, in detail to a defined standard, during debrief sessions, with the procedure open.

In the absence of a full scope simulator, the second part of this objective could be achieved by using the method suggested in the preceding example of start-up of the unit. However, the first part of this objective poses a greater problem since OJT is not an option. Use of less than a full scope simulator is possible but again must be augmented with classroom sessions and main control room walkthroughs of the procedure.

Clearly, a full scope simulator is the best setting in which to realize this objective. However, it must be remembered that it is the realization of the objective which is the essential feature of the training programme; not necessarily the means to that realization.

Human factors related training objectives also need to be incorporated. An example of such a training objective is shown below:

By the end of the training programme, the trainee control room operator will be able to:	undertake his correct role, as defined in plant procedures, as part of the control room team in all aspects of plant operation.

Again a full scope simulator is the best setting in which a trainee can achieve this training objective. However, the objective can also be achieved through a combination of classroom, OJT and multifunctional simulator training.

6.3.3.3. Components of training programmes based on simulation — for NPP personnel other than control room operators

The analysis phase of SAT may identify a number of NPP jobs requiring KSAs in plant operation. The corresponding training programmes could benefit from simulator training. The positions most likely to benefit from this type of training are:

42

- Shift technical advisers
- Shift supervisors
- Field operators
- Managers
- Nuclear engineers
- Instrumentation and control technicians
- Off-site technical support personnel
- Human factors specialists
- Procedure writers
- Instructors
- Regulators.

While for some jobs the most useful device may well be the same simulator that is used for operator training, other types of simulator such as those described in Section 6.5.3.1 can be successfully used in training personnel for the jobs listed above. The use of a device other than a full scope control room simulator for training these personnel may be more effective.

The list below, while by no means exhaustive, is meant to illustrate the potential uses of simulator training and to motivate plant management to consider it for training of personnel other than control room operators.

Instrumentation and control technicians	Reactor protection system simulators can achieve objectives associated with trouble shooting and fault diagnosis. They have the capability for fault insertion and subsequent diagnosis and rectification. Simulators of the full scope, replica type are preferred.
	Simple simulations of control loops and their associated transducers can be achieved with either full scope or part task simulation.
	CBT based simulation of three term controllers can be used to show the effects of changing gain.
Radiological protection personnel	Health physics instruments can be replicated to respond to simulated signals, rather than to radiation, thus allowing training in their use without contravening ALARA principles.
	Contamination can be very simply simulated by using fluorescent material and instruments (replicating health physics instruments in appearance).
Mechanical maintenance personnel	Mock-ups of plant equipment or actual excess plant equipment can be used to simulate the work place.

Electrical maintenance personnel	A simple example of simulation for the training of such staff involves the use of actual electrical protection equipment to simulate electrical system faults.
Field operators	Refuelling machine simulators are used for some NPPs. For others, refuelling machine consoles have a 'simulation' mode which can provide realistic training on some operations of this equipment.
Chemistry technicians	At some NPPs, water treatment plants have their own control rooms. Multifunctional simulators may prove to be cost effective in circumstances where long periods of OJT are not appropriate.
Electrical control room personnel	At some NPPs, grid system operations are carried out from a dedicated control room. Full scope or multifunctional simulation may prove to be cost effective in training for grid system disturbances and electrical protection equipment operation.
Management and emergency support personnel	Some operator training simulators are interfaced with on-site technical support centres and emergency off-site facilities. This permits use of the simulator as a tool for emergency preparedness training of personnel.

6.3.4. On the job training (OJT)

OJT represents the largest proportion of the training of almost all NPP personnel training programmes. OJT requires special attention because of its importance in helping trainees to achieve a large number of training objectives, and also because OJT is generally provided by part time instructors. There are different types of OJT. Some of the types are:

- Shadowing job incumbents in a particular job and observing demonstrations as to how tasks should be performed;
- Performing particular tasks under the supervision of a qualified person;
- Systems tracing;
- Plant walkthroughs;
- Observation of specific scheduled events.

SAT based OJT is a systematic method of ensuring that trainees obtain required job related KSAs in the actual work environment. It is not just working in the job/position under the supervision of a qualified individual. It involves the use of training objectives, training guides, qualification standards and trainee assessment. It provides hands-on experience and allows the trainee to become familiar with plant routines while being trained. This training should be conducted and evaluated in the work environment in a consistent way by qualified, designated individuals.

The terminal objective example below would be suitable for OJT because there are no operational constraints that would preclude training to achieve this objective in the plant. Also, it would not be feasible to build a full scale simulation or mock-up of this equipment:

Subject and Verb	Object	Conditions	Standard
Upon completion of the training programme, the trainee will be able to point out	each component and connection in the condensate system from the suction of the condenser extraction pump to the suction of the main feed pumps	while tracing the system in the turbine hall	identifying all components and connections with 100% accuracy, in a time of 40 minutes

The following should be taken into account when selecting OJT as the training setting:

- Training should be done in small groups;
- There should be no significant constraints (due to plant conditions) preventing accomplishment of the training objectives;
- Actual performance of tasks/training objectives during OJT should be encouraged, with walkthroughs of the tasks/training objectives as an alternative;
- Qualified personnel should be available to conduct and supervise the training and to assess the performance of trainees.

6.3.5. Computer based training (CBT)

CBT has already been referred to in support of other settings, such as in the classroom or for self-study. In this section, it is considered separately owing to the increasing attention it is receiving. As with other training settings, CBT should be selected only when it provides an efficient, cost effective way to achieve training objectives.

Reasons for the increasing importance of CBT are:

- The training can be adjusted to individuals' schedules, independently of the availability of instructors and other trainees' schedules;
- A trainee can adjust the training duration (including repetitions of some sections) to his ability to fully understand the presented material;
- In many instances, the more efficient use of training time allows shortening of the duration of individual modules and so reduces training costs;
- Instructors have more time available to help trainees with the most difficult parts of the training programme because they do not have to lecture throughout the whole module;
- CBT software can be designed to include testing programmes which include automatic scoring and record keeping;
- Clearly, cost is a major consideration in the selection of a training setting. For certain types of training objectives common to a number of plants, CBT can be cost effective owing to the large population of potential trainees.

When considering CBT as a possible training setting, one must be aware of its potential shortcomings, including:

- CBT systems can be costly to upgrade in the event of changes in regulations, plant systems, and procedures;
- Costs for CBT systems vary greatly from one country to another and can sometimes be very expensive, especially in the case of interactive video systems;
- For specific applications, CBT systems cannot be produced without a team of designers that should include, at a minimum, highly qualified subject matter experts (SMEs), graphics designer(s) and software engineer(s); guidelines for CBT system designers are necessary.

At present, CBT accounts for only a small fraction of training provided in even the most advanced NPP personnel training programmes.

6.3.6. Laboratory, mock-up and workshop training

A laboratory, mock-up or workshop training setting is selected to provide a training environment that is similar to the trainee's future job environment. Generally, laboratory/workshop training allows the following:

- Simulation of realistic job conditions;
- Learning actual skills required on the job;
- Training to apply knowledge to solve realistic problems;
- Supplementing classroom training with detailed knowledge and skills needed for component and system repair and maintenance;
- Training in basic skills that support task performance.

Mock-ups of plant equipment or actual spare plant items can be useful in achieving some training objectives. For example, a steam generator channel head can be placed in an environment which simulates plant conditions in terms of layout and access, temperature and noise (not radiation and contamination). Also, 'just in time training' can be facilitated by the use of such equipment in the event that steam generator entry becomes necessary.

6.3.7. Self-study

Self-study (also referred to as self paced or individualized instruction) is any training in which trainees learn at their own pace without the continuous presence of an instructor. Self-study includes:

- Reading textbooks and other written training materials;
- Individual research or problem solving exercises;
- Computer based instruction, and other similar techniques.

Although continuous instructor supervision is not required, an instructor should be available to assist trainees and should periodically assess their progress.

Self-study may be the training setting chosen if sufficient training material is available and the nature of the training objectives is appropriate for self-study. In general, self-study is well suited for fundamentals training, training on system or component descriptions, and as a supplement to classroom training.

When self-study is applied to in-plant training, there must be assurance that no danger exists for trainee injury or equipment damage and that meaningful training can be carried out without continuous instructor supervision. The tasks to which self-study may be applicable are of a simple nature and do not require sophisticated and expensive facilities, components, or materials.

6.4. CONTINUING TRAINING REQUIREMENTS

6.4.1. General

There are two main categories of continuing training:

- Refreshing those training objectives from initial training for which competency is not maintained through working on the job. Examples of such training objectives are those supporting tasks important to safe plant operation which are infrequently performed, such as those related to response to abnormal or emergency conditions.
- Training on changes in plant design, plant procedures and regulatory requirements, and on operational experience feedback.

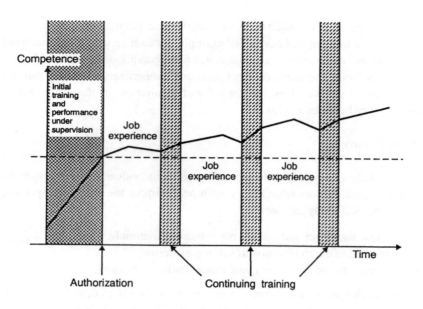

FIG. 6.3. Competence development through continuing training.

The goal of continuing training is, therefore, not just to maintain competence but also to enhance those competencies that are required for the safe, reliable operation of an NPP. Figure 6.3 shows graphically how continuing training relates to the competence development of NPP personnel. This figure shows that there is generally an upward trend in the competence of personnel after completion of initial training. However, for some areas of the job, there is a need for periodic continuing training to maintain this level of competence.

6.4.2. Control room operators and shift supervisors

A typical example of the need for continuing control room operator training is in the mitigation of emergency situations. The following are examples of training objectives related to this continuing training need. The first is for the control room team, and the second only for the shift supervisor.

Upon completion of this simulator exercise, the control room team will be able to:

Diagnose and mitigate the consequences of any design basis accident, followed by the necessary actions, according to the procedure, with assistance from a shift colleague reading the step by step instructions.

Upon completion of this simulator exercise, the shift supervisor will be able to:

During a design basis accident, supervise the actions of control room operators, communicate with all on-site and off-site agencies and declare the appropriate level of emergency, according to the procedure.

Experience has shown that the continuing training for control room operators should have the following characteristics:

- The frequency should be at least twice per year;
- The duration should be three to five working days per occasion;
- The total time spent on continuing training should not detract from the achievement of 50 to 100 hours of simulator continuing training per year (including briefings and debriefings).

It is important for continuing training to reinforce appropriate use of plant procedures and, for control room operators in particular, communication according to procedures. There is also some merit in rotating team members through various positions, as this can aid in the realization of objectives associated with interpersonal skills and because it allows a better understanding of the relationships within the team. Many control room simulators allow for communication and hence role playing between control room personnel and support groups (e.g. maintenance and radiation protection personnel). It is of great benefit to continuing training if, on occasion, management and technical support personnel (who may be required to be in the control room in an actual emergency) enact the roles in the simulator scenario which they would play in an actual plant situation.

It can be useful if the assessment of trainees is performed by the instructor and the shift supervisor. This is one way to ensure that the same standards of performance are being applied by the NPP and the training organization.

With respect to classroom training, some operating organizations have found it useful to refresh parts of initial training on a cyclical basis throughout continuing training. This is recommended in the areas of thermodynamics, reactor physics, fluid mechanics and electrical theory for control room operators. Pretesting of trainees before continuing training is recommended to demonstrate that refreshing of items in the cognitive domain is necessary. Continuing training on these theoretical topics should be related to applicable plant systems and characteristics, so that the relevance of the training to operations can be shown.

6.4.3. Maintenance personnel

For maintenance personnel, the same two continuing training categories apply as for operations personnel:

- Refreshing those training objectives from initial training for which competency is not maintained through working on the job;
- Training on changes in plant design, plant procedures and regulatory requirements, and on operational experience feedback.

However, the 'just in time training' approach has been used at some NPPs as an alternative to refresher training at fixed intervals. This approach provides training for activities/tasks just before their being performed on the job. It is particularly suitable for infrequently performed tasks that can be scheduled well in advance, such as maintenance performed during outages.

6.4.4. Other NPP personnel

It has been common practice for NPP personnel to claim that they maintain competence in all aspects of their jobs through working regularly on the job. However, the degradation in competence in some aspects of a job over time, shown in Fig. 6.1, is applicable to all NPP personnel groups although the impact on operations personnel is probably the most pronounced.

6.5. IDENTIFICATION OF TRAINING MODULES THAT APPLY TO MORE THAN ONE JOB

6.5.1. General employee training

The most obvious requirement for common training for NPP personnel, contractor personnel and visitors is the safety training needed for unescorted access to all or parts of the plant. This is usually known as general employee training.

Analysis of training needs for general employee training will identify a range of KSAs in the field of industrial safety and in the ability to respond correctly in the event of emergencies. The degree of knowledge required in these subjects (industrial safety; fire protection; emergency response; health physics; plant design, organization and access procedures to non-radioactive parts of the plant) depends on the group to which the employees belong. This degree may be defined in terms of two categories:

Category 1: This knowledge enables a person, after a short introduction on site, to perform a task inside the non-radioactive part of the plant without having to be guided or supervised continuously.

Category 2: This knowledge enables a person to supervise others and to introduce them to their area of work.

Those personnel whose duties require them to work in radiation and/or contamination zones will also require additional training in the radiation safety procedures they must follow when entering, working in and leaving these zones.

Many plants provide continuing general employee training at intervals of every one or two years both to refresh initial training and to inform personnel about changes in requirements or lessons learned.

6.5.2. Basic theory and plant design

Much of the knowledge in basic theory (e.g. heat transfer) and in plant systems (e.g. reactor coolant system) is required, in whole or in part, for several different NPP jobs. Courses can be tailored to allow for a number of personnel with different jobs to train together on these topics as long as the training objectives apply to all the jobs. Training can be more efficiently conducted by increasing the number of trainees in such shared modules.

6.5.3. Human factors and other competencies common to NPP personnel

The human factors competencies categories below apply to most NPP jobs and hence training objectives and modules designed to train on these competencies should be suitable for many different groups of personnel. Section 5.9 provides additional details on these human factors competencies:

- Communication
- Team building
- Management and supervision
- Leadership
- Analytical methods
- Man–machine interface.

6.6. ENTRY LEVEL REQUIREMENTS OF TRAINEES

Figure 6.4 shows the relationships among job competence requirements, entry level requirements and training programme content. Job competence requirements (KSAs) are determined from the analysis phase. Trainee entry level requirements (education, experience, prior training) are established by plant management based upon a number of factors, principal among which are the educational qualifications of

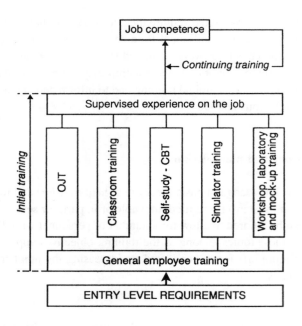

FIG. 6.4. Paths to job competence.

available personnel. The difference between job competence requirements and trainee entry level requirements is what must be provided by initial training programmes. Continuing training programmes provide the closed loop that ensures that job competence is continually updated and maintained above minimum standards.

An accurate determination of trainee entry level KSAs ensures that training begins at an appropriate level and unnecessary training is avoided. Specification of the required educational level of job candidates, while important, is not sufficiently specific to determine whether particular KSAs should be entry level requirements or should be included in the training programme. In many cases, it is necessary to estimate the extent of trainee entry level KSAs needed for the job, and to verify these estimates later by pretesting actual trainees before programme implementation.

6.7. DESIGNING TEST ITEMS AND CONSTRUCTING TESTS

For each training objective, one or more test items should be produced. Tests may be examinations (written or oral) or practical demonstrations of acquired skills

52

(in the case of on the job, laboratory, or simulator training). Plant walkthroughs are used in assessing knowledge of the location or identification of systems and components. Performance demonstrations should involve actual performance of a task whenever practicable. Simulated performance should take place under conditions that are as realistic as possible.

Assessment of those control operator KSAs which cannot be assessed in the plant is performed by simulator exercises which allow trainees to demonstrate the ability to deal with normal, abnormal, and emergency plant conditions. In addition to assessing individual trainees, simulators are used to assess an operating team's ability to perform effectively as a team.

In addition, the training programme design should prescribe the assessment method for each module and for the final examination. For example, the training programme may prescribe the following for each module:

- Daily (or weekly) progress tests should be administered to evaluate the effectiveness of the training and to reinforce training when trainees have had difficulties in achieving certain training objectives;
- Written or oral examinations should be scheduled at the end of each module;
- To successfully complete a module, the trainee must receive a final average grade of usually 70 or 80%, or above, on the written or oral examination.

6.8. ESTIMATING RESOURCE REQUIREMENTS

The final step in completing the training plan is to estimate the resources required for the development and implementation of the initial and continuing training programmes (e.g. instructors, training material developers, plant personnel, facilities and equipment). This estimate is important as a project management tool. When the available resources are less than the estimated resources required, revisions to the training plan should be considered.

It is only at this point in the SAT process that a detailed schedule can be finalized and specific resources identified/committed for the development of training materials.

7. DEVELOPMENT

7.1. INTRODUCTION

The purpose of the development phase is to produce the materials needed for the implementation of initial and continuing training programmes. All training materials should be consistent with plant documentation. For example, where items such as system descriptions exist in a suitable format, it is preferable that certain material for systems training is based on them. Figure 7.1 shows the inputs to and outputs from the SAT phases through the development phase.

Figure 7.2 shows the relationships between the training plan from (the design phase) and the module and lesson plans (from the development phase). Module and lesson plans detail the activities that are outlined in the training plan.

7.2. MODULE PLAN

The training plan produced in the design phase specifies a number of modules that together make up a training programme. It is usual to set up a document structure as shown in Fig. 7.2, to control the development process down to the most detailed level of documentation required. The first item required is a plan for each module which allocates the associated training objectives to lessons of appropriate duration. (In some countries, the term 'training course' is used instead of, or in addition to, 'training module'.)

The purpose of the module plan is to provide an overview of the module and to maintain the master copies of the documents.

The following items are generally contained in the module plan:

- Purpose of the module in terms of a list of terminal and enabling objectives to be realized, and their allocation to lessons;
- Expected trainee entry level skills and knowledge in the form of programme/ module prerequisites;
- Timetable;
- Requirements for implementation;
- Applicable set of examination questions;
- Evaluation standard forms;
- Record of approvals;
- Record of amendments/modifications.

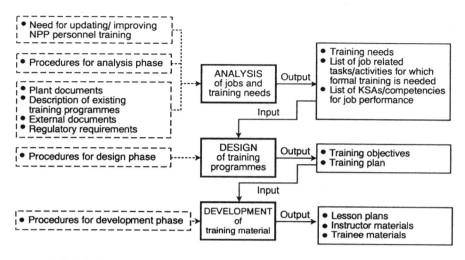

FIG. 7.1. Inputs and outputs of the analysis, design and development phases.

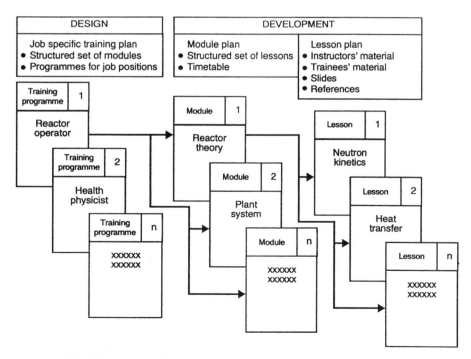

FIG. 7.2. Relationships between training plan and module/lesson plans.

7.3. LESSON PLAN

The purpose of the lesson plan is to allow an instructor to prepare for, and then conduct, a training lesson using only this plan.

The following items are generally included as part of the lesson plan documentation:

- Requirements for implementation (e.g. classroom, overhead projector, basic principles simulator, number of instructors, etc., for the particular lesson);
- Training objectives to be realized in the lesson;
- Trainers' material (this should include any references to such items as textbooks);
- Trainee material (this should include any references to such items as textbooks);
- Examination questions for the topic;
- Any portable audiovisual aids (e.g. overhead projection transparencies);
- References (e.g. plant procedures and maintenance instructions);
- Record of approvals;
- Record of amendments/modifications.

Instructor material tends to be different for different training settings. Also, lesson plans for continuing training will generally be different from those for initial training. In the following sections, examples of typical instructor materials are given for classroom and simulator lessons. In general, trainee material should conform to the following guidelines irrespective of training setting.

Trainee material guidelines

- Charts, graphs, tables and other illustrations emphasizing key points should be located within the text and in close proximity to the related information and should be sequenced according to the visual aids used by the instructor.
- The reading level of training materials should be consistent with the expected entry level skills of the trainees.
- Objectives should **always** be provided to trainees as part of written training materials.
- The material should be clear, accurate and concise.
- In general, essential information should be located in the materials, and the trainees should not be referred to other places for that information. However, training materials should not repeat or include plant specific information that is included in controlled plant documents and is subject to change, but should contain references to those plant documents.
- The training materials should refer to the job for which the trainees are being trained by describing that job environment, how the information will be applied to the job, and why it is important for the trainee to learn that information.

- Transparencies and slides are commonly used to supplement instructor explanations. Copies of them should be included as part of the written material given to the trainees, if this material does not include them as illustrations.
- Trainee material must be consistent with, and have a close connection to, instructor material.

7.4. CLASSROOM TRAINING

7.4.1. Trainee material

Written materials used by trainees during a training programme will normally be either textbooks or trainee materials developed specifically for the programme. Textbooks are rarely totally satisfactory as a means of mastering training objectives. Invariably, they will contain irrelevant or superfluous information, and they may not be easy to obtain in some countries. They will, however, provide a useful source of information for those involved in the development of training material and particularly in support of theoretical topics such as reactor physics and thermodynamics. Textbooks can be useful as references in support of trainee material, to reinforce learning. However, rarely is it appropriate to develop a textbook in support of a training programme.

Generally, it will be found more effective and efficient for written materials to be produced in support of a series of training objectives to be covered in a single training lesson.

7.4.2. Instructor material

The most important documents specifying the training activities are the **lesson plans**. They are used by the instructor to guide the learning process and to outline instructor and trainee activities. They ensure consistency in delivering lessons among several training instructors and from one class to another. Typically they are of a two column format, shown in Table 7.1.

7.4.3. Selection of audiovisual aids

A variety of audiovisual aids are available. They include films, videotapes/videodisks, multimedia computer based training as well as slides and transparencies.

The following list represents those training aids in common use in training centre classrooms.

- Chalk boards;
- Overhead projectors and transparencies;

TABLE 7.1.   EXAMPLE OF LESSON PLAN FORMAT

Key words and instructor activities	Support information and anticipated or planned trainee activities
State objectives (Use slide 1)	Go through each objective in turn. Trainees must know precisely what is required of them at the end of the lesson.
Overview whole system (Use slide 2 — diagram of system)	In this column, all the components with technical details could be listed, e.g. pump capacities, where the electrical supplies are located, etc. It should contain slightly more information than the requirement to meet the objectives as there could well be detailed questions from the trainees and it is useful for preparation.
Components in the system (Use slide 3 — picture of first pump)	Detail in here as to where it is located and other pertinent facts.
(Use slide 4 — pump connections)	This is a line diagram to show the positioning of components with respect to each other. Detail of connections and valves associated with first pump in the system.
Ask questions, such as: Where is the first pump located?	Detail the answers in this column, some or all of which may be of use during the presentation.

- Photographic projectors and slides;
- Film projectors and films;
- Videocassette players and either visual display unit or video projector;
- Audio equipment and cassettes;
- Scale models (helpful in learning the characteristics of major plant components; usually they either have a cutaway section to help in visualizing the internal parts of the component or they can be disassembled to reveal them).

Those training aids involving visual movement, e.g. videos, are frequently used to illustrate specific plant activities such as refueling, maintenance, transport of heavy components, etc. The videodisk has the benefit of permitting a very fast search for specific sequences and is often integrated with computer based training for self-paced study. However, the necessary hardware and software are expensive.

The advantage of using films and video is the ability to provide to trainees information that would be difficult to transmit otherwise. To maximize the benefit of such training aids, they must be integrated into a structured lesson and duly referenced in the lesson plan.

Factors to be considered when selecting training aids include:

- The projected life-cycle costs of the selected training aids are lower than other equally useful aids.
- Budgetary resources are available, particularly if the training aids require a substantial capital investment.
- The training aids are appropriate for the number of trainees who will be trained at a given time.
- The training aids are appropriate for training that is subject to frequent change or is conducted infrequently (if applicable).
- The lead time to produce the training aids is compatible with the time-scale for implementation of the training.

Choices should be made on the basis of a balance between training effectiveness and cost effectiveness. For example, assume that there is an annual demand for a two day module whose objectives can be adequately met by two instructors using overhead projection slides. There would be little point in producing a video, the cost of which would be much higher.

7.5. SIMULATOR TRAINING

In developing material for the conduct of simulator training, the following factors should be addressed:

- Time allocated for the presentation of the scenario, coaching the trainee, performing the scenario, monitoring the performance and obtaining feedback from the trainee(s). These are usually referred to as brief, monitor and debrief sessions.
- Approved trainers' material, including lesson plans. (In the case of simulator training these are very often referred to as scenario guides.)
- Approved trainee material.
- Simulator lessons incorporating rotation through positions and role playing.
- Available plant documents (e.g. emergency operating procedures, normal operating procedures, technical specifications, communications procedures).
- Audits of procedures to ensure they are consistent and up to date.
- Feedback to plant with respect to any conflict encountered.
- Availability of the means to contribute to the overall evaluation of training programme effectiveness and suitable means of data collection on lesson effectiveness.

7.5.1. Trainee material

Material should be substantially different for different types of training lesson. For example, an initial training simulator module for control room operators early in their training programme will have requirements different from those for a continuing training lesson for an experienced shift team. An initial training lesson's material may include specific objectives associated with, for example, the control of boric acid concentration in the primary circuit of a PWR. It may contain diagrams, possibly simplified, and technical information regarding control rod worth and boric acid worth. For continuing training, a shift team may only be given the broad goal of taking over shift and continuing with an evolution according to procedures.

Trainee material for simulator training should give preferred solutions to operational problems encountered during scenarios.

Usually a plant referenced simulator will be used for the latter stages of initial and continuing training for control room operators. (Different types of simulation devices may apply for the initial and continuing training of maintenance personnel.) When this is not the case, materials must emphasize the differences between the simulated plant and the actual plant of the trainee. The differences need to be expressed not only in terms of plant design features and procedures, but also in the potential difference in realizing the same objective by different means between the two 'plants.'

7.5.2. Instructor material

Instructor material needs to contain information about the simulator as well as about the achievement of objectives. A simulator user manual is clearly required, but individual simulator lesson plans should also include special instructions regarding maintenance of the validity of the simulation.

In the case of a simulator exercise, it is essential that the lesson plan (sometimes called a scenario guide) contain sufficient information on how to operate the simulator. All exercises should be prepared in advance and run through, in real time, to check satisfactory simulator performance and adequacy of the simulator lesson plan.

For full scope simulator exercises, lesson plans should be agreed with NPP management. The simulator, as in the case of the plant, must be operated in accordance with formal procedures provided by plant management. Simulator lesson plans must reflect and reinforce the operating standards of the NPP, such as use of procedures and rules for communication.

Materials need to be available to allow the instructor to perform efficiently the pre-exercise briefing and post-exercise debriefing (brief and debrief) as well as the scenario itself. The materials contain such information as:

- Previous power history
- Plant conditions

- Evolutions in progress (e.g. plant startup)
- Equipment out of service
- Abnormal equipment line-ups
- Plant maintenance history

There are numerous variations for the format of simulator lesson plans. Typically, they use a four column format. A simulator lesson plan for a simple evolution is shown in Table 7.2 as an example of how such a format could be used.

TABLE 7.2. EXAMPLE OF SIMULATOR LESSON PLAN

Progress of the evolution	Instructor activity	Expected trainee activity/response	Notes: such as questioning required, special observations to make, particularly difficult concepts
Insert control system malfunction to fail pressurizer relief valve open	Observe trainees.	Reactor operator notes alarms recede and should correctly diagnose a control system fault; informs supervisor; accesses procedure.	
Reactor coolant system pressure falls	Observe pressure rate of fall and trainee responses.	Reactor operator takes remedial action according to the procedure. Supervisor confirms the diagnosis and informs I&C.	
	Observe how well pressure limits are maintained.	Reactor operator continues to control pressure using manual control.	Question supervisor concerning satisfaction with the remedial action taken.
	Telephone reactor operator as a nuclear engineer and request details of plant main parameters.		Ensure that the shift team do not become distracted by the query.

7.6. ON THE JOB TRAINING

The experience of IAEA Operational Safety Review Team missions has been that the implementation of on the job training (OJT) in many utilities has been inferior to the standards achieved in other training settings. One of the reasons for this has been the absence of adequately developed trainee and instructor material. Another is that detailed procedures for the evaluation of OJT are not usually available.

7.6.1. Trainee material

In some instances of OJT, it may be adequate to issue a trainee with a list of the terminal objectives to be achieved. For other sessions, it may be necessary to develop specific assignments in the form of a work book so that more complex objectives may be achieved.

7.6.2. Instructor and assessor materials

In the following suggestions are provided for improving the effectiveness of OJT (while many of these have been discussed in the earlier parts of this section, they are explicitly stated below in view of the significance of OJT in achieving staff competence to operate a specific NPP with its own particular systems and layout):

- Training objectives, including performance standards, must be defined and explained to the trainees, trainer and assessor.
- The assessor should not be the same person as the trainer. Training and assessment materials need to be developed to facilitate this division of responsibilities.
- The OJT guide should list the materials which should be available to the trainee for use during training and assessment.

7.7. LABORATORY, MOCK-UP AND WORKSHOP TRAINING

Mock-ups that are full scale sections or assemblies are especially suitable for teaching some of the skills required by maintenance personnel. They permit practice of an operation or procedure until competence has been achieved. Activities to be conducted in radiation zones can be practiced and hence the exposure time minimized. A mock-up in common use is the end of a steam generator incorporating the correct access geometry such that entry to conduct tube inspections can be practiced.

7.7.1. Trainee material

When training on mock-up equipment, plant procedures should be used if at all possible. Similarly, during maintenance training in the workshop environment the actual maintenance instructions for the activity being performed should be available.

7.7.2. Instructor material

Instructor material should be similar to that provided for OJT since the aim of these settings is to simulate actual plant conditions as far as practicable. Also, the format of the material should be consistent with that for OJT.

7.8 COMPUTER BASED TRAINING (CBT)

Material developed for CBT is usually integral to the software associated with the actual conduct of the training. A substantial portion need not be written documentation. Clearly, a portion will always need to be written; for example, instructor material will need to include an equipment manual and instructions for operating the CBT system.

Trainees' material should include the following:

- Training objectives
- CBT users' guide

The training objectives need not necessarily be in paper form, but as with all training settings the achievement of training objectives remains the paramount feature of a training lesson.

Material for both trainer and trainee will need to be tailored to the type of CBT system to be used and the topic to be addressed. For example, some of the simpler lessons consist of little more than screen scrolling, i.e. electronic page turning. It may be adequate for the trainee to have little more than a 'print screen facility' under these circumstances. In the case of more complex systems employing multimedia and possibly some form of simulation, the development of appropriate material will need to be considered in the design phase when the training setting is chosen.

7.9. SELF-STUDY TRAINING

Strictly speaking, self-study does not represent a training setting, as it can be conducted in the plant, in a workshop, at a computer terminal in the home or in the work place. Material should therefore be appropriate to the actual setting in which the self-study takes place. If, for example, systems tracing or plant walkthroughs require that a trainee have unescorted access to particular plant areas, then sufficient supervision must be built into instructor material, and safety instructions must be built into trainee material.

7.10. REVIEW OF TRAINING MATERIALS

Material developed for use in training programmes must be reviewed before its use, to ensure completeness, technical accuracy and support of the training objectives. Whenever possible, the material should be tested in advance of actual implementation by using a small group of trainees or other personnel.

The goal of the review is to ensure that training materials:

- Are technically accurate and current;
- Achieve training objectives;
- Support the learning process.

The review must be undertaken by an expert or experts who provide(s) feedback to the programme developer. Lesson plans, text material, trainee material and workbooks, audiovisual media and test items should be reviewed and deficiencies identified for correction.

7.11. TEST ITEM VALIDATION

Each test item should be validated. Validation is usually performed in three stages:

- Peer review/assessment validation panels.
- Pilot course analysis.
- Continuous analysis of trainee results. This is particularly important for early implementations of new courses/modules.

For the first of the above stages, it is useful to prepare a checklist regarding the properties of a valid question. Examples of these properties are:

- To which training objective does the item relate?
- Is the model answer correct and does it appropriately relate to the training objective? (A 'model answer' is the answer necessary to obtain full marks for the associated question)
- Is the question consistent with other questions to be used in the same assessment?
- Is it clear to a potential trainee what portion of the total score is assigned to the question?

- Is the question clear and unambiguous?
- Does the model answer contain a clear, unambiguous marking scheme with alternative, partially acceptable answers to those considered 100% correct?

7.12. REVIEW OF TRAINING MATERIAL USE

After revisions from the review described in Section 7.10 have been made, the training materials should be tried out on a small group of trainees or others who possess the entry level requirements expected of future trainees. During this preliminary use of the training materials, the actual environment in which the training is to be conducted should be simulated as closely as practicable. The training materials should be presented as intended for actual use, and all tests should be administered and scored. Data should be collected for subsequent analysis and used to improve lesson plans, trainee material etc. as well as to check the instructor's teaching skills.

It should be recognized that preliminary conduct of training may not always be feasible, particularly with modules of lengthy duration. An alternative is to conduct small-group tests on the most important sections of the module. Modules or parts of modules not submitted to small-group review should receive increased monitoring during their first implementation.

Results from the preliminary conduct of training are valuable in determining the extent to which the training achieves the intended training objectives. Failure of the trainees to achieve satisfactory test results may necessitate revision of the training materials or teaching methods. However, in the event of low scores, care must be taken to check that the test items do relate to the job related KSAs and hence to the training materials used in the lessons. Completion of post-training questionnaires by the trainees, supplemented by interviews, should be used to provide data to assist in the evaluation of training programme difficulty, length, clarity, terminology, pace and structure.

8. IMPLEMENTATION

8.1. INTRODUCTION

Training implementation is the conduct of training using materials and lesson plans developed during earlier phases. Hence, the most relevant input to this phase is the trainees. Similarly the most relevant output is competent personnel. Figure 8.1 shows these and the other inputs and outputs.

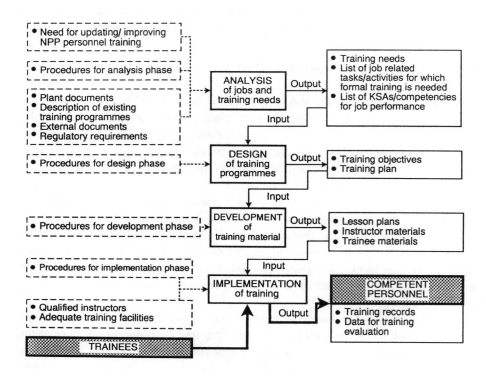

INPUTS   SAT PHASES   INPUTS/OUTPUTS

- Need for updating/ improving NPP personnel training

- Procedures for analysis phase

- Plant documents
- Description of existing training programmes
- External documents
- Regulatory requirements

ANALYSIS of jobs and training needs — Output →
- Training needs
- List of job related tasks/activities for which formal training is needed
- List of KSAs/competencies for job performance

Input

- Procedures for design phase

DESIGN of training programmes — Output →
- Training objectives
- Training plan

Input

- Procedures for development phase

DEVELOPMENT of training material — Output →
- Lesson plans
- Instructor materials
- Trainee materials

Input

- Procedures for implementation phase

IMPLEMENTATION of training

COMPETENT PERSONNEL

- Qualified instructors
- Adequate training facilities

Output
- Training records
- Data for training evaluation

TRAINEES

FIG. 8.1. Inputs to and outputs from the implementation phase.

8.2. GENERAL

In preparing to implement training, it is necessary to establish conditions which allow trainees to give maximum attention to the training process. This can be achieved by releasing the trainees from all job duties while in training and by selecting a suitable time for the training sessions. Training after normal working hours, on weekends and during vacation periods is generally less efficient and effective than training during normal working hours.

The efficiency, effectiveness and impact of the training also depend on the availability of a suitable training environment. There must be sufficient light, adequate heating, cooling and ventilation facilities, and very little outside disturbances. It helps also if some recreation and refreshment facilities for trainees are available in the vicinity of the training area.

66

There are four distinct activities in the implementation of training:

- Instructor preparation to conduct training
- Pretesting trainees
- Conducting training
- Assessing trainee performance.

8.3. INSTRUCTOR PREPARATION

Before conducting each lesson of a training module, instructors must be provided time to prepare delivering that lesson. It is common practice to provide an experienced instructor with preparation time approximately equal to the time required to present the lesson. If training materials need to be modified, then additional preparation time needs to be provided. During preparation, the instructor should review the total content of the lesson (in accordance with the lesson plan) and identify the parts which need more attention or special explanation. The instructor must review the status of training facilities and materials (procedures, drawings, textbooks, examinations, tools, media, models, simulator, classroom facilities and equipment) needed in training. Any correction or repairs to training materials or facilities should be completed prior to the start of the training session.

In the case of simulator training, the instructor must check that the state of the simulator is satisfactory for conducting the training, e.g. no defects are present which would inhibit the satisfactory achievement of the objectives. If in doubt or if the exercise is new to him/her, he/she should arrange to go through the lesson plan using the simulator. He/she should also satisfy himself/herself that up to date copies of all documentation available in the power plant control room are also available at the simulator facility for use by the trainees. (Note: this would only apply if the simulator were a plant referenced simulator.)

In addition to reviewing the lesson plan, all instructors should review the procedures for monitoring progress and trainee tests relevant to that particular portion of training.

8.4. PRETESTING TRAINEES

Trainees must meet established entry level requirements for the training programme or module in order for them to achieve the training objectives. When the backgrounds and competence of trainees are **not** accurately known in advance, a pretest should be administered before starting the training. The information obtained from such pretests is important to guide the instructor on how best to achieve the objectives, and to identify planned training that may be unnecessary for particular trainees.

Specifically, the pretest results can be used for:

- Confirming that individual trainees meet the entry level requirements for the training programme.
- Identifying necessary additional (i.e. remedial) learning needs for the trainees who did not satisfy the entry criteria.
- Identifying parts of the training programme for which an accelerated schedule could be applied owing to confirmed trainee mastery of the subject material.
- Identifying parts of the previous training programme where objectives have not been satisfactorily met or where trainees have not retained the information.
- Providing information for programme effectiveness evaluation.
- Defining a learning strategy on the basis of weaknesses and strengths of a particular group of trainees.

For situations where the backgrounds of trainees are well known (e.g. recent graduates of a technical university or school with programmes of known content) pretesting may be unnecessary.

8.5. CONDUCT OF TRAINING

8.5.1. Conduct of classroom training

The lesson plan defines training objectives, instructor and trainee activities and the main resources needed to support training. For classroom training it is imperative that instructors state the training objectives at the start of the session and review them again at the end of the session.

To deliver good training, the instructor must be fully familiar with the subject of the lesson and with the relation of the subject to the terminal objectives. The lesson must be delivered clearly and concisely. Practical examples are very useful, particularly if they are directly related to the subject of the lesson.

It is equally important to find ways to maintain trainee interest in, and attention to, the lessons. Some useful ways are:

- Involve trainees in the learning process by encouraging discussion.
- Ask questions of the trainees when some important facts are introduced in the lesson (to maintain trainee interest and to confirm that they understand the material that has been presented).
- Connect important subjects of the lesson with actual plant experience.
- Speak slowly and clearly.
- Do not make the lessons too long.
- Remove potential sources of external noises and visual distractions during the lesson.

- Avoid overloading the trainees with duties associated with their work, because this will create anxiety and distract them from the training.
- Use rewards to recognize achievements (appraisals, certificates, etc.) and encourage co-operation among individuals and among groups of trainees.
- Make available to trainees in a timely manner training material covering exactly the subject of the lesson, to avoid the distraction of taking detailed notes.

Effective classroom training depends upon the availability of sufficient time between lessons to allow trainees to review the content of past lessons, to consolidate the knowledge and to prepare for the following lesson. In implementing a training programme, a balance should be sought between classroom training periods and periods reserved for trainee self-study. In addition, classroom training should be alternated with practical training (e.g. on the job or simulation training).

Classroom training can often be enhanced by the use of appropriate media such as audio and video devices and mock-ups of plant components.

8.5.2. Conduct of simulator training

Simulator training using appropriate lesson plans should be implemented in three parts:

- Pre-exercise briefing (or brief)
- Simulator exercise
- Post-exercise debriefing (or debrief).

Full scope simulator team training should generally be conducted with the same number of people who will be in an actual team on the job. Simulation devices of less than full scope are appropriate for developing individual skills and team skills that do not require full scope simulation.

Usually, a plant referenced full scope simulator will be available for both initial and continuing training of control room operators and supervisors.

The examples discussed here generally refer to operating personnel; however, there are also examples of simulator training for other personnel which would require a similar set of activities. One such example is the use of reactor protection system simulators for I&C technicians.

8.5.2.1. Pre-exercise briefings

Simulator training is more effective when, before the exercise, the trainee(s) is (are) introduced to the training objectives and provided a review of prerequisite knowledge. Any principles or procedures that will be used should be made clear. The exception to this approach is when the purpose of the exercise is to provide practice in responding to unannounced malfunctions or to assess trainee performance.

Any simulator characteristics that differ from what would be expected at the plant should be brought to the attention of trainees.

During the briefing, all relevant plant history should be made available to trainees. It is useful to conduct shift turnover in accordance with the plant procedures. Such procedures generally require that information such as the following is made available:

- Previous power history
- Plant conditions
- Evolutions in progress
- Equipment out of service
- Abnormal equipment line-ups.

Briefings need not take place at the simulator and may be better scheduled to occur in a classroom containing suitable training aids, etc.

8.5.2.2. Simulator exercises

The manner in which the exercise is conducted should vary according to considerations such as:

- Trainee's job;
- Where the lesson is sequenced in the overall training programme;
- Whether the exercise is for training or evaluation;
- Whether it is initial or continuing training.

In the case of full scope, plant referenced simulators, realism should extend to the use of normal protocols for communications and to the use of actual plant procedures. In the case of a non-replica simulator, suitable protocols/procedures which are representative should be adopted. Section 6.5 refers to the good practice of dividing initial simulator training into a number of modules which can be interspersed with OJT in the plant control room. In this way, reinforcement is provided throughout the programme on the team member's role in the control room and the need to observe control room protocols and procedures.

Simulator instructors must take on various roles for different stages of initial operator training, ranging from coach/mentor to assessor. These various roles will necessitate different exercise guides for the same basic simulator scenarios. The number of instructors involved in conducting a simulator exercise should be sufficient to accomplish the simulator operation, instruction, role playing and trainee assessment activities defined in the lesson plan/exercise guide. Some simulator exercises, particularly those involving trainee assessment, will require two or more instructors.

The importance of using plant procedures for simulator training cannot be overemphasized. Procedures may have limitations and thus should not be followed blindly. Rather, procedure use should be coupled with an ongoing, logical thought process.

Thus, there must be emphasis on teamwork and diagnostics training in both initial and continuing training programmes. Also, the use of a plant referenced simulator for the validation of new procedures is extremely useful from three points of view:

- Operating personnel feel responsible for the procedures;
- Procedure changes can, with appropriate care, be trained for ahead of implementation at the NPP;
- Procedures are validated from both the human factors and technical standpoints.

8.5.2.3. Post-exercise debriefings

A debriefing should be conducted after each exercise to reinforce appropriate responses and to correct weaknesses. This may involve rerunning portions of the exercise or using the monitored parameters function of the simulator to show what happened during the exercise. Instructor observations made during simulator exercises may be supplemented during the debriefing by questioning trainees to determine their level of knowledge. A debriefing technique that many instructors have adopted is to first let trainees debrief the exercise, and then to provide any additional comments that were not addressed by the trainees. This technique is less threatening and adversarial than a debrief led only by instructors.

Videotape recordings can make a useful contribution, particularly when reviewing teamwork on a replica simulator.

For control room operator training, it is beneficial, when reviewing emergency training scenarios, for the instructor to promote a discussion which extends beyond the potential emergency, in order to highlight:

- Essential operator actions and safety system responses to mitigate threats to the barriers against fission product release.
- Accident management strategies and emergency plan arrangements.
- Validity of procedures particularly in the area of symptom based procedures. (This is particularly useful for continuing training of control room operators. It provides an additional means for the feedback of procedure related information to the NPP.)

Trainee assessment during simulator training is addressed in Section 8.6.2.

8.5.3. Conduct of on the job training

The persons who implement on the job training should be individuals currently qualified for, and working in, the positions for which the trainees are being trained. In addition, they should receive instruction on the proper methods of conducting such training and should understand their role in the training process. This includes understanding:

- Overall concept of on the job training;
- Methods of developing required trainee knowledge and skills;
- Methods of performing trainee progress assessments;
- Application of established standards in the trainee assessment process;
- Action to be taken when the trainees do not satisfy the assessment criteria;

When assigning job incumbents as trainers for OJT, attention should be paid also to their human factors KSAs, such as communication skill, judgement, personal maturity and general attitude to training and to assigned tasks.

A selected individual (usually from the training department) should be in charge of co-ordinating OJT. Some of the main co-ordination duties are to:

- Follow the training schedule and assign milestones in the training process;
- Monitor trainees' progress;
- Provide training materials;
- Co-ordinate training assignments to take advantage of opportunities to train on infrequent work activities;
- Document the training process;
- Evaluate training effectiveness;
- Maintain documentation.

On the job training can be divided into three main phases:

- Preparation;
- Demonstration and practice;
- Assessment.

The first two phases will be discussed here. The assessment phase of OJT is discussed in Section 8.6.3

8.5.3.1. Preparing the trainee for OJT

The trainee is prepared for on the job training by being familiarized with all relevant information such as:

- Instruction in the use of the materials;
- Target dates to complete particular parts of the training;
- On the job training checklists, training objectives and references;
- Supporting study materials (drawings, flow diagrams, procedures, system descriptions, etc.);
- All necessary industrial and radiological safety precautions.

Reference materials should contain all necessary data on systems or components included in the training (descriptions, functions, precautions for their operation and/or maintenance, safety limits, alarms, controls, trips, interlocks, normal and abnormal operating modes, etc.). In addition to studying training material, the trainee should review important items with the trainer.

8.5.3.2. OJT demonstration and practice

Before any demonstration, the trainer explains its purpose, appropriate procedural steps, the consequences of improper performance, current industry practices relevant to a particular item of the demonstration and answers trainee questions. If plant conditions allow, the trainer demonstrates how to perform the activity.

The practical work of the trainee follows these demonstrations. This work, depending on the nature of OJT, consists of:

- Performing the particular task, under supervision (for example, the startup of a circulating water pump or the dismantling and repairing of a component or instrument);
- Walkthrough of the activity with a qualified trainer.

The trainer corrects observed performance deficiencies and helps the trainee to improve his skills.

When the trainee and trainer are confident that the trainee has mastered a specific item of the training programme and that the trainee is able to meet the relevant training objectives, an assessment of the performance is requested to be made by a designated assessor.

8.5.4. Conduct of laboratory, mock-up and workshop training

Many aspects related to the conduct of both classroom and OJT are applicable to laboratory/workshop training. In many situations, this setting is a more favourable environment for learning a skill, e.g. fault finding in an electrical circuit, than the OJT setting. As with all training activities, the conduct will be in accordance with an approved lesson plan to achieve the training objectives and will be undertaken by a competent, experienced instructor. The safety of trainees must be maintained throughout the session. This can best be achieved by ensuring that adequate prerequisite safety training has been built into the overall training programme and that the ratio of trainees to instructors allows close supervision to be provided.

The size of groups of trainees in the laboratory/workshop should be such that every trainee has the opportunity for hands-on practice. While this can be maximized if trainees work as individuals, small groups are usually beneficial to the learning process through the trainees' sharing of progress and knowledge in a co-operative manner. In addition, the high cost of equipment or mock-ups may necessitate group work.

The introduction to a lesson will play just as important a role in a laboratory or workshop as for a classroom lesson. Trainees' attitudes will in all cases be greatly influenced by the first few minutes of the lesson. As with all training, it is imperative that the trainees understand the objectives and duration of the session, how it will be structured, the opportunities available for practice and the method and standards for assessment.

The lesson plan should include, in its introduction, a review of prerequisite KSAs before presenting the material for the session. This section of the training will often take place in a classroom near the laboratory or workshop. Trainee materials will include all written materials the trainees need (or references as to where it can be found), together with a list of tools and/or equipment they will utilize. At some point the instructor will demonstrate the task, building on knowledge and skills previously acquired.

During hands-on practice by the trainees, the instructor must be alert to all the trainees and move steadily around all individuals or groups. The instructor should make use of oral questioning to ensure that important aspects are adequately understood by the trainees. On occasion, this feedback may cause the instructor to stop the exercise and to disseminate information to all trainees. Throughout the session the instructor should help, encourage and, if necessary, demonstrate particular techniques more than once.

In concluding a lesson the instructor should discuss or review:

- The entire task, to tie together the separate items learned in the lesson;
- Questions raised by trainees;
- Problems that arose in conducting the practical exercise and ways in which they could be solved;
- References and suggestions for further study and practice;
- Class progress;
- How the work relates to the next lesson.

8.5.5. Conduct of computer based training (CBT)

CBT modules are generally designed for independent learning. However, experience has shown that trainees generally require support during CBT. An instructor's role is normally to monitor trainees' progress through the module, to detect difficulties at an early stage and to deal with them.

CBT software will normally incorporate intermediate as well as final assessments. Instructors and trainees should, therefore, be able to obtain reports on trainee progress via simple interrogation of the CBT system.

8.5.6. Conduct of self-study training

Although self-study modules are designed for independent learning, trainees may still require support from trainers, supervisors and/or colleagues.

As with all training settings, self-study modules should be based on training objectives and well defined learning tasks which should be clearly stated to the trainee. The support person's role is normally to monitor trainees' progress through the module, to check that they are up to date with their work, to detect problems or difficulties at an early stage and to deal with them. A variety of self-study situations exist, for example:

- Self-study of training materials to reinforce instruction received in a classroom or similar setting;
- Self-study of training materials in a training setting or centre;
- Self-study at home;
- Self-study in the work place, e.g. plant systems training.

The support and monitoring arrangements will vary according to which self-study method is used.

In addition to assisting with difficulties and problems, the designated support person should be able to assist in the location of suitable supplementary resources such as reference material.

8.6. ASSESSMENT OF TRAINEE PERFORMANCE

Assessment of trainee performance during, and at the completion of, training is an essential component of the training process. These assessments are necessary to determine whether trainees are achieving the training objectives and to verify that they have achieved the competence required to perform the job for which they have been trained. The assessments also give feedback information to training instructors and plant management on the effectiveness of the training programme and data on the success in the selection of trainees for that particular training. The feedback information from the assessment should be used to make improvements in the training programme as necessary (see Section 9).

Trainee performance and progress during training should be monitored closely and continuously. The data for this progress monitoring should be derived not only from tests, but also from daily discussions, questions during lectures, performing practical work, etc.

Trainee performance must be assessed regularly during each module and at the completion of the training programme, according to consistent standards and as scheduled in the training plan. The schedule for the tests should be known in advance by trainees.

All examinations, whether concerning simulator performance, plant walk-through or simple multiple choice tests, must be based only on the training objectives derived in the design phase of SAT. This applies equally to external licensing or any other type of procedure to authorize personnel to do a particular job.

The test items and tests to be used for trainee assessment are developed during the training programme's design phase. Assessments used to verify competence upon completion of training should be related as much as possible directly to actual job tasks performed in the job environment (with normally available tools, procedures, etc.). Examinations are a convenient mechanism for measuring how effective the lessons have been. They are either progress tests during the conduct of the training or final examinations.

Test results should be provided to trainees as soon as possible after testing. Test results should then be reviewed jointly by the instructor and trainee. Deficiencies should be identified and advice provided to trainees on necessary improvements. Trainees not meeting pre-established standards should not be allowed to progress to the next stage of training until deficiencies have been corrected.

8.6.1. Assessment of trainee performance during classroom training

The following assessment methods, while suitable for almost any training setting, are discussed here because they are commonly used in the classroom training setting.

8.6.1.1. Written examinations

Written examinations have the advantage of enabling the instructor to examine a large group of trainees simultaneously and of allowing sufficient time for trainees to work out numerical examples, draw diagrams and sketches, and describe answers. Additionally, written examinations provide documentation of trainee performance. One limitation of written examinations is that some individuals (especially those with lower educational levels) have difficulty in expressing their knowledge clearly and in a logical sequence in a written form.

Written examinations usually use one or more of three types of question:

- **Multiple choice questions.** Multiple choice questions are easy to administer and enable a large number of knowledge items to be tested in a short period of time. They are particularly useful to measure the recall and comprehension levels of intellectual ability, but need care in their formulation.
- **Short answer.** Short-answer questions require the trainee to provide a phrase, sentence or diagram as a response. They have the benefit that, unlike multiple choice questions, no stimulus by way of possible answers is provided.
- **Essay.** Essay questions provide the most satisfactory written means of assessing a trainee's competence at high levels of intellectual ability. While essay questions based on objectives included in the training programme are relatively easy to develop, their judging and grading takes longer and is more difficult than with the other two types of question.

8.6.1.2. Oral examinations

As with written examinations, oral examinations must be carefully prepared and reviewed to ensure that they accurately assess trainee competence in relevant topics and achievement of training objectives. This includes preparing the questions in advance and ensuring that each question is job related (i.e. related to a specific training objective).

Indicating the key items expected in answers will help in maintaining objectivity and provide for immediate feedback to the trainee when the correct answer is not obtained.

When a response requires the use of training materials, plant documents, drawings, training aids and/or some component, care must be taken to ensure that these are made available to the trainee in due time, or that he knows that he is responsible for obtaining these in order to answer the question.

Oral examinations should be well documented. Examination forms should be prepared for each trainee. These should contain a description of question areas, a summary of the content of acceptable responses and the assessor's remarks. The examination forms should be filed as examination records for future use.

The advantages of oral examinations are:

- They give almost unlimited possibility to the trainee to express in his own words his understanding of the topic.
- They give the assessor a better insight into the trainee's overall knowledge and allows him to investigate more deeply the trainee's understanding of the subject through additional questions. (In this instance care must be taken to retain objectivity).
- They provide immediate feedback to trainees when an incorrect response is given.

The disadvantage of oral examinations are:

- Individual assessment of each trainee may not allow sufficient time, e.g. to work out calculations or to develop systems diagrams.
- Quality and effectiveness of an oral examination depends on the examiner's skill. Therefore, it is recommended that several qualified examiners participate in the final certification oral examinations.
- There is a risk of personal bias, of inadequate sampling of the trainees' knowledge, and of the interference by factors not related to the training criterion.
- One effective assessment approach for classroom training is to combine written and oral examinations, thus taking advantage of the benefits of both.

8.6.2. Assessment of trainees in simulator training sessions

Effective simulator training requires that individual and team performance be assessed during and at the completion of training programmes. During the programme, the information is valuable for measuring trainee achievement of training objectives and providing guidance on areas of weakness which can be addressed during subsequent training. Assessment during a simulator exercise should be conducted in as objective a way as possible.

Performance based objectives can be tested by a number of means including the following types of simulator assessment technique:

- **Static assessment.** In this type of assessment, the simulator is frozen in a particular configuration. Students are required to investigate the log, VDU formats, mimic panel indications, etc. to determine the current simulator conditions, what faults currently exist, what technical specification limits are being breached, etc.
- **Dynamic assessment.** In this type of assessment the student is briefed to carry out a particular operation (or maintain steady conditions). The simulator instructor then monitors the student and, in some cases, generates malfunctions. The instructor will monitor/evaluate the student's performance against criteria associated with the following:

Awareness
Event diagnosis
Immediate/entry level actions
Subsequent actions
Desk and panel operations
Technical specification and other documentation
Communications
Supervisory skills
Team skills
Use of procedures.

Depending on the stage of the training, some or all of these areas will be assessed. On some simulators, computerized logging/recording of trainee actions and major parameters can be used to assist the assessment.

8.6.3. Assessment of trainees in OJT

Performance demonstrations are used to measure the skills and knowledge acquired by trainees through OJT (as well as through simulator, workshop or laboratory training). Performance demonstrations generally require the trainee to demonstrate proficiency in a specific activity using appropriate procedures, tools and equipment, as necessary. Performance demonstrations should be as realistic as possible.

Ideally, performance of the actual activity is required. If plant conditions or other limitations do not allow this, then a walkthrough or simulation of the activity should be used for the assessment.

The person designated for the assessment must be an experienced person, preferably not the individual involved in the conduct of on the job training for the particular trainee being assessed. The assessor should provide all the information that the trainee would have for actual task performance, but coaching, or other forms of assistance, should not be allowed.

The trainee assessment process can be described by the following sequence:

- The training assessor schedules the assessment.
- The assessor conducts an assessment of acquired trainee KSAs achieved in training using the pre-established evaluation standards and objectives.
- If the assessor finds the KSAs of the trainee satisfactory, he provides written confirmation of this satisfactory assessment. If not, he directs the trainee to upgrade his KSAs by further training.
- The assessor provides feedback to the training department on any necessary improvements in OJT on the basis of deficiencies detected during trainee assessment.

8.6.4. Assessment of trainees in laboratory/workshop training

Unlike OJT, the assessment of performance will often be conducted within the laboratory/workshop session, and not as a separate session using an independent assessor. Thus, it should always be clear in advance whether the instructor's observing and questioning is part of the formal assessment process or is part of the teaching technique intended to help the trainee achieve the training objectives.

8.6.5. Assessment of trainees in CBT

CBT software will normally incorporate intermediate as well as final assessments, in order to determine achievement of training objectives. CBT systems often allow pretesting of trainees, in order to identify the training objectives for which training may be required. This is a particularly useful capability for continuing training.

8.6.6. Assessment of trainees in self-study

The method of assessment will depend on the training media used. For all self-study methods, the traditional oral and written methods of assessment are relevant, plus plant walkthroughs if, for example, the self-study has been associated with establishing knowledge of power plant systems and their location. In the case of oral assessment and plant walkthroughs, the assessor should not be one of those providing support during the self-study sessions. As with all training, it is important that adequate records of the competencies achieved by the trainees be established and maintained.

8.7. FEEDBACK

Trainees should be provided with prompt, regular and objective feedback on their performance from any assessment method. The test results from written tests should be scored and returned to the trainees, preferably within a day, but in no more than a week. Test results should then be discussed in a critique session to point out weaknesses and to indicate areas of necessary improvements.

Identification of trainee weaknesses is relatively straightforward. Finding the causes of those weaknesses is not as simple, and more training is not always the solution. One method of identifying weaknesses is careful evaluation of the aggregate results of oral, written and performance tests in order to identify potential areas of weaknesses, both in the training and in the testing methods. If some of the test items are frequently answered incorrectly, this may indicate a weakness in the training programme, and not in the trainees. This subject is discussed in detail in Section 9.

In addition to feedback provided for overall performance assessment, feedback should also be provided on specific KSAs that do not meet job performance requirements.

8.8. PERFORMANCE BELOW REQUIRED STANDARDS

Trainees who perform below required performance standards should be provided with remedial training and retested. Trainees should be removed from the training programme if, after remedial training, the required standards are still not met. Methods to be applied when trainees cannot meet performance standards should be defined in appropriate written procedures.

Trainees should not be allowed to proceed to a higher training level before their performance at the lower level is satisfactory. Since the training is normally held for a group of trainees, the time available for individual remedial training is often rather limited.

When the root causes of the difficulties are identified to be in the initial training programme, special training techniques should be used to correct them. This would require careful analysis of the original training programme, including inputs from trainees and graduates of the programme. Information regarding trainee deficiencies should also be used as feedback into the overall programme evaluation (see Section 9).

Similarly, job incumbents performing below required standards during requalification or continuing training should be removed from the associated job duties and provided with remedial training. Continued failure to achieve required performance standards will necessitate the removal of the individual from the training programme and the job.

8.9. TRAINING RECORDS

The establishment of a training records system is an essential part of a properly implemented training programme. Two types of records are needed:

- Records of the training programme as implemented.
- Records of individual trainee performance as assessed.

Records of the training programme as implemented will include details of the actual schedule and trainee attendance, training facilities used, trainee materials, lesson plans and examination questions, as specified in the QA programme of the NPP.

For each trainee, data on his progress should be recorded. This should include indication of training programmes completed, any special qualifications received (e.g. radiation worker, QA auditor, OJT assessor) as well as test and examination results associated with these training and qualification programmes.

As discussed in Section 9, the above information, as well as instructor and trainee inputs, are needed for training programme evaluation. The collection of this information should be done by the instructor responsible for the training programme and reviewed by the trainee's supervisor.

9. EVALUATION

9.1. INTRODUCTION

The purpose of the evaluation phase of SAT is to determine the effectiveness, efficiency and impact of training programmes and to identify whether and where revisions or improvements are needed. Figure 9.1 shows the inputs to, and outputs from, all SAT phases. It emphasizes that the SAT process is not complete without the evaluation phase. This figure also shows that the evaluation phase provides a strong linkage to the NPP in terms of both inputs and outputs.

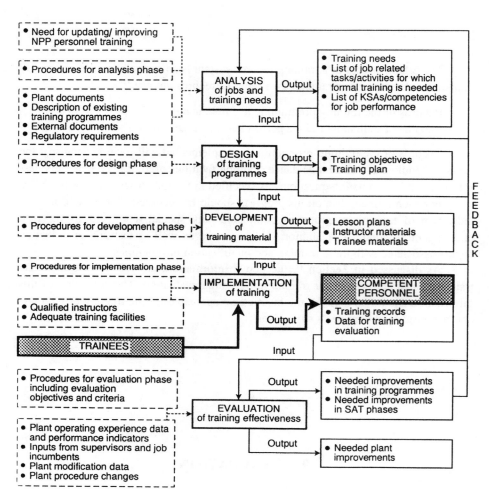

| INPUTS | SAT PHASES | INPUTS/OUTPUTS |

INPUTS

- Need for updating/ improving NPP personnel training

- Procedures for analysis phase

- Plant documents
- Description of existing training programmes
- External documents
- Regulatory requirements

- Procedures for design phase

- Procedures for development phase

- Procedures for implementation phase

- Qualified instructors
- Adequate training facilities

TRAINEES

- Procedures for evaluation phase including evaluation objectives and criteria

- Plant operating experience data and performance indicators
- Inputs from supervisors and job incumbents
- Plant modification data
- Plant procedure changes

SAT PHASES

ANALYSIS of jobs and training needs

Output

Input

DESIGN of training programmes

Output

Input

DEVELOPMENT of training material

Output

Input

IMPLEMENTATION of training

Output

Input

EVALUATION of training effectiveness

Output

Output

INPUTS/OUTPUTS

- Training needs
- List of job related tasks/activities for which formal training is needed
- List of KSAs/competencies for job performance

- Training objectives
- Training plan

- Lesson plans
- Instructor materials
- Trainee materials

COMPETENT PERSONNEL

- Training records
- Data for training evaluation

- Needed improvements in training programmes
- Needed improvements in SAT phases

- Needed plant improvements

FEEDBACK

FIG. 9.1. Overview of SAT process including inputs and outputs.

82

9.2. ROLE OF EVALUATION

This section takes a broad view of evaluation as a tool to improve the effectiveness of training through promoting quality. It also demonstrates the integral role of evaluation in SAT and in the ongoing functioning of a nuclear power plant. There are two, complementary aspects to training programme evaluation:

- Internal evaluation by the plant and training organizations;
- Independent review by external organizations.

Internal evaluation should be integrated with other SAT activities to become a continuous part of the overall system. Thus, the ideal answer to the question: "How often are training programmes evaluated?" is: Continuously. Evaluation can occur at any time and for any phase of the SAT process; it takes the pulse of the current system. Current levels of performance are compared to standards. If a discrepancy is revealed, two follow-up activities are undertaken:

- Determine the importance of the discrepancy (is it important enough to justify additional effort to correct?)
- Cause analysis (what are the reasons for the discrepancy?)

The second, complementary aspect of training programme evaluation is **independent review**. This review is likely to be performed by a combination of organizations external to both the plant and training organizations including: international organizations such as WANO or IAEA, national organizations such as regulatory bodies and industry organizations, and quality assurance or independent review organizations established by the NPP operating organization. These independent evaluations should be viewed as a way to validate conclusions drawn by the internal evaluation process and to improve the training programme evaluation process.

'Ownership' of (responsibility for and commitment to) evaluation activities is an important consideration. Specialists may be assigned to assist in and co-ordinate the evaluation process, but the 'owners' of the evaluation process need to be those who are responsible for the activity being evaluated (e.g. full time instructors, part time OJT evaluators). For example, an instructor who has presented a training module should consider that he or she is responsible for the evaluation of the effectiveness of the module. Instructors may secure the help of other individuals in collecting or analysing the evaluation data, but they need to feel that it is their training programme, and they are responsible for identifying ways to improve it.

The following are the characteristics of training programmes that are evaluated through the evaluation process:

Training needs. Does training meet the established needs?

People (instructors, trainees, assessors). Does the quality of performance meet established standards?

Materials and tools. Is the quality of these products fit for their purpose?

Processes. Are training and qualification processes (e.g. scheduling, assessment) being implemented as intended?

Purposes. Are they clearly defined? worth while?

Facilities and resources. Are they adequate to support training activities?

Costs. Are they justified by the benefits provided?

Impacts. Is training improving the job performance to which it is related?

9.3. INTERNAL EVALUATION

Continuous internal evaluation should be the cornerstone of training programme evaluation, not something that is done every year or two to prepare a formal report. This means that internal evaluation should be an integral part of every training activity, whether it is analysis, design, development, or conduct of training.

Experience from those NPPs that have implemented SAT based training for their personnel shows that the most useful information for training programme evaluation can be obtained from the following sources:

- Plant operational experience feedback/performance indicators;
- Industry wide operational experience feedback;
- Reports from inspections and evaluations;
- Changes in plant procedures and descriptions of plant modifications;
- Input from plant supervisors;
- Input from job incumbents;
- Input from instructors;
- Input from trainees;
- Data from observation of training and plant activities.

These inputs and their use in evaluation are discussed in the following sections.

9.3.1. Plant operational experience data/performance indicators

Plant performance is highly dependent on NPP personnel performance. Thus, plant performance is a good indicator of the effectiveness of training programmes. However, there are many factors other than training which also affect plant performance. For example, a high plant capacity factor could also mean that while there may be a weakness in training in a particular area, it is being compensated for by some other factor (such as procedures or close supervision). Conversely, a decreasing, or low, capacity factor does not necessary mean that training programmes are poor. Other factors, such as equipment design, could be responsible for this performance deficiency. The point here is that plant operational experience provides the evaluators with indicators of what aspects of training should be examined, but does not confirm that training programmes are either adequate or inadequate.

NPPs should make every effort to analyse events in order to identify underlying human factors based root causes. The results of such analyses must be fed back into relevant training programmes and other affected areas (e.g. procedures, equipment design, organization). Useful information about which aspects of training should be scrutinized can be provided by: review of experience in handling abnormal operating conditions and plant transients; and data on the number of plant trips, equipment failures, unscheduled maintenance, plant availability and work practices, and frequency of personnel errors (particularly those for similar or related events).

Some plants have developed a set of plant specific training performance indicators, either as a 'stand-alone' system, or as part of a larger system for plant performance indicators. If such indicators are available, they should be regularly monitored, and the results used as inputs for training programme evaluation.

9.3.2. Industry wide operational experience feedback

Industry wide operational experience can be used in the same way as plant operational experience to evaluate training programmes, while providing the benefit of learning from other's experience. There is a tendency to dismiss experience of other plants on the basis that they are different from the plant in question. However, if the information is viewed from the perspective of "a similar situation which could happen at any plant", useful information can often be obtained, even from plants of quite different design. It can be a valuable exercise to determine the methods and systems that are in place at the plant to prevent a situation which occurred at another plant.

Sources of information on nuclear industry experience include reports on operating and maintenance events distributed through national and international channels (e.g. operating organization associations, owners groups, IAEA, WANO, reactor vendors), as well as participation in industry activities such as peer reviews, and plant to plant visits. Obviously, review of industry events provides lessons learned for all plant activities, not just training. Thus, at some plants the function of reviewing industry events for applicable lessons learned is co-ordinated by a central group in the NPP.

9.3.3. Reports from inspections and evaluations

Nuclear power plant inspections to evaluate plant safety and reliability can provide a valuable source of information on training programme effectiveness. The inspections and evaluations referred to here are not only those whose principal focus is training. Almost any evaluation of plant activities has potential relevance to training. For example, an inspection of reactor protection system maintenance might conclude that technicians performing calibration checks of the equipment were damaging the detectors when they removed their test equipment. This deficiency may be a result of inadequate training, but it might also be a result of other factors, such as excessive workload causing technicians to rush the work, or because of poor work habits due to inadequate supervision or attitudes. Training programme evaluation should provide the tools to identify when training solutions to performance deficiencies are needed and, equally important, when solutions other than training are needed.

9.3.4. Changes in plant procedures and descriptions of plant modifications

A system needs to be established which routinely provides information on proposed plant modifications and procedure changes to the training organization for action. Training programmes need to include a component related to changes in plant procedures and plant documents (e.g. procedures, technical specifications, technical manuals). For initial training, the evaluation phase should ensure that training materials are based upon the current versions of plant procedures and equipment. For continuing training, job incumbents should be trained before revised procedures become effective, or new/modified equipment is put into operation.

9.3.5. Input from plant supervisors

A formal method to periodically request and receive supervisor feedback on job performance should be an integral part of training programme evaluation. Supervisors are well qualified to identify on the job performance problems and anticipated changes in job requirements. They should also be consulted periodically on how well training is preparing new employees to perform their jobs and what continuing training is needed for current employees. The following is specific feedback that should be collected from supervisors:

- Tasks for which recent graduates are inadequately prepared;
- Types of error committed by job incumbents;
- Suggestions for improvement in initial and continuing programmes.

9.3.6. Input from job incumbents

A formal programme for collecting feedback from job incumbents after they complete training should be implemented. Typically, a survey or structured interview would be conducted three to six months after completion of training. The following is the specific feedback that should be collected from job incumbents:

- Tasks for which additional training was needed in order to perform the task correctly;

- Difficulties experienced in performing on the job;
- Differences between task performance and how the task was taught during training;
- Changes in the job since the incumbent was assigned to it;
- Training which has not been used on the job;
- Suggestions for improving training.

9.3.7. Input from instructors

Section 8 describes methods for assessment of individual trainee achievement of training objectives. This section focuses on using the aggregate of this information for evaluating the overall training process not only through assessments of trainees but also through an evaluation of the various components of the training provided by the instructor. If the data indicate that a significant fraction of trainees had difficulty in meeting a particular training objective (as measured by examination/evaluation of trainee performance) an evaluation should be initiated to determine whether or not additional or alternative methods should be used for training on this particular objective.

9.3.8. Input from trainees

Trainees provide first-hand feedback on the training which they have received. Thus they can make a valuable contribution to evaluating training programmes. The types of feedback which they can and should provide include:

- Adequacy of time allotted for training;
- Organization of training to facilitate learning;
- Views on whether training objectives were achieved;
- Adequacy of training materials, instruction and facilities;
- Relevance of training to job performance.

9.3.9. Data from observation of training and plant activities

Many plants have programmes to observe regularly the conduct of both training and plant activities. Personnel assigned to perform these observations should represent a broad cross-section of those parts of the plant organization (departments, divisions, groups etc.) affected by the activity being observed. In some cases, these are organized self-assessment programmes where observations resulting from these assessments are reported and corrective actions are identified. It is necessary to ensure that these corrective actions are implemented in a timely manner. Other plants have less formal systems such as 'management by walking around', where managers and supervisors are expected to spend a certain number of hours per week observing the conduct of activities for which they are responsible.

These programmes may or may not include any formal monitoring and follow-up of issues identified and their corrective actions. Where these programmes for observing training and plant activities exist, they provide an important source of information for training programme evaluation and for feedback.

These types of observation provide a particularly good opportunity for joint participation by plant departments and training organizations. In this way, both the NPP and the training organization can ensure that they are applying the same standards of performance in the plant and in training settings.

9.4. INDEPENDENT REVIEW

Independent reviews provide an opportunity to 'calibrate' both the NPP's and training organization's views of how well training is being provided. Independent reviews should never be seen as a substitute for internal evaluation. Independent review teams bring another perspective to the evaluation of training programmes. Thus, their views are important. However, their conclusions and recommendations need to be challenged and weighed in light of the overall programme.

Independent review teams should not be put on a pedestal, but should rather be considered as peers who have an objective and complementary function and perspective. If their suggestions and observations are not clearly understood, or are considered to be in error, they should be challenged in a positive way. Similarly, it is counterproductive intentionally to keep information from an independent reviewer. It is appropriate to present information in a positive way and to offer explanations for substandard performance. It is inappropriate intentionally to mislead or keep important information from independent reviewers. The value of the information provided by independent reviews is directly related to the professional and open environment established for the conduct of the review. As was indicated earlier, the conclusions from outside reviews should be integrated with other evaluation results to identify necessary training programme changes and plant improvements.

Preparation for an independent review is particularly important. Often independent review teams have very limited time in which to conduct their review. They may either misunderstand what they have heard, or may have incomplete information. Thus, it is important that independent review teams work closely with both plant and training organizations. There should be regular interactions to share preliminary conclusions, and also to request additional information. In this way, misunderstandings can be resolved early, and conclusions based on incomplete information can be avoided. The plant should have a professional and open relationship to independent review teams.

Regulatory audits are one type of independent review that deserve particular mention because there is often a reluctance to share information with the regulator. This makes it more likely that misunderstandings will occur. The plant and training organizations need to work hard to establish a climate where there are no secrets concerning the training programmes and the lessons learned concerning their effectiveness. Mutual trust between the regulator and the operating organization is a very valuable commodity. If it exists it is much easier to resolve issues and agree upon corrective actions. A regulator that is well informed about the status of and basis for plant training and qualification programmes is much less likely to feel a need for continual examinations, inspections, reports and other regulatory activities which can be very time consuming and burdensome.

Some countries — where NPPs have implemented SAT based training programmes — have established agreements between the plants and regulators indicating that SAT based training will be required for NPP personnel. These agreements have replaced regulations which specified details of training programme content, or hours of training on a particular topic. The regulator then conducts independent reviews/audits of the NPP's training programmes to validate the quality of implementation of the SAT process. The frequency and rigor of these inspections is adjusted based upon the quality of training programmes (as determined from previous reviews/audits, plant performance and plant documentation).

A typical regulatory review or audit of a SAT based training programme would look both at the quality of performance of graduates of the training programme, based on observation and review of plant documentation, and at the quality of training provided. For any job performance weaknesses identified, inspectors would focus particularly on training related to the job performance. A determination would then be made as to whether a training weakness and/or a weakness in some other plant programmes/systems contributed to the job performance weakness.

9.5. FEEDBACK OF EVALUATION RESULTS

Feedback involves providing information from the results of evaluation, especially that related to needed improvements, to the person/organization responsible for the function. The continuous evaluation process then ensures that these improvements are implemented in a satisfactory and timely manner. Figure 9.2 shows key elements of the SAT evaluation phase including feedback of needed improvements.

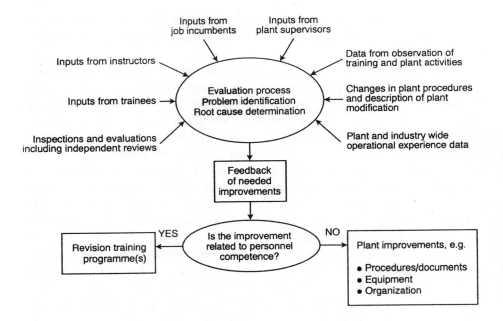

FIG. 9.2. Key elements of the evaluation phase.

If the feedback process is continuous and integral to all SAT activities, then the use of evaluation results to confirm, improve or modify training programmes is almost automatic. However, there is nothing that will damage an evaluation programme quicker than not using evaluation results to make needed changes in a training programme. Conversely, if plant personnel see that their inputs are seriously considered and used to improve training and qualification programmes, they are more likely contribute actively and constructively in evaluating subsequent programmes. Further, it is important to provide feedback to individuals who offer their suggestions, particularly if these suggestions are not implemented. If they are not provided with this feedback, they will assume that their inputs are not valued, and they will be less inclined to participate meaningfully in subsequent evaluation efforts.

In addition to identifying needed improvements or modifications in training programmes, the evaluation phase may also identify any necessary plant improvements, such as improvements in plant procedures and other documentation, plant or training department organization and interfaces, and/or plant/training equipment. Methods need to be established to ensure that this information is provided to the responsible individuals and that there is a follow-up of needed improvements to their successful completion.

9.6. TRAINING PROGRAMME EVALUATION OBJECTIVES AND CRITERIA

The following objectives are suggested for the purpose of developing criteria that can be used for evaluation of SAT based training programmes. The list of criteria associated with the objectives are examples of possible criteria which could be used based on those objectives.

1. Training programme description and content

Objectives: Training programmes are established to provide nuclear power plant personnel with appropriate technical and human factors KSAs necessary to perform functions associated with the position for which training is being conducted.

Initial training prepares trainees to perform independently the job for which they are being trained.

Continuing training maintains and improves incumbent job performance.

Criteria: 1. A systematic approach to training is used to identify, establish and maintain the training programme content. Existing information in the form of guidelines, procedures, training materials, etc. should be taken into account in the identification of training programme content.

2. The initial training programme is based on the performance requirements of the job for which training is being conducted. The consideration of job performance requirements should include an analysis of both the technical and human factors KSAs required for effective job performance.

3. The continuing training programme maintains and improves the KSAs of job incumbents and includes programme evaluation feedback, regulatory changes, changes in job scope, results of external evaluations and inspections, changes to relevant industry documents, changes in procedures, changes in unit/plant systems and equipment, similar unit/plant experience, results of root cause analyses, equipment and personnel performance trends, and industry experience.

2. Organization and management of training

Objective: All training activities are effectively directed and adequately supported by management of the operating organization.

Criteria:
1. Plant management is responsible for the competence of NPP personnel and for ensuring their effective training and qualification.

2. Line management supports the training process to ensure that training and qualification programmes will produce competent NPP personnel.

3. The goals of training are clear and are supported throughout the operating organization.

4. The responsibilities and authorities of personnel involved in managing, supervising, and implementing training are clearly defined in writing and permit effective control of training activities.

5. Policies and procedures to implement a systematic approach to training are defined and used as the primary means for the management of NPP training programmes.

6. Training is adequately funded and staffed to develop and maintain competent NPP personnel.

7. Managers ensure that personnel complete required training.

8. Personnel complete desired training and qualification requirements before being assigned to work independently. Completion of training requirements by equivalent education or experience should be documented and approved.

9. Initial training programmes are used to train and qualify replacement personnel.

10. Contractors or other non-plant personnel are appropriately qualified to perform assigned duties.

11. Training records are maintained to support information needs.

3.   Development and qualification of staff with training duties

Objectives: Training staff members (plant and contracted, if used) possess the requisite knowledge, experience, and skills required to fulfil their assigned duties.

Criteria:
1. Training personnel meet and maintain the educational, technical, and experience qualifications required for their respective positions.

2. Training programmes develop and maintain the necessary instructor capabilities to fulfil training programme requirements in all applicable settings.

3. If occasional instruction is provided by personnel without formal training in teaching KSAs, the training is monitored by qualified training personnel.

4. Personnel who conduct on the job training and assessment are cognizant of the policies, practices, methods, and standards for conducting on the job training and assessment.

5. Instructor performance is assessed regularly and the results are used to improve performance.

6. Continuing development of training personnel maintains and improves needed technical and teaching competence.

4.   Analysis

Objectives: Potential training needs are systematically analysed as a basis for training actions.

An inventory of plant specific tasks/competencies that are the basis for training programmes is complete and current.

Criteria:
1. A plant specific task/competency inventory, developed from a job analysis performed by NPP personnel, training staff, and other appropriate subject matter experts, is available.

2. Job scope changes, unit/plant changes, procedure changes, unit/plant and industry operational experience, and feedback from other sources are analysed for additions, deletions, or modification to the task/competency inventory.

3. Tasks/competencies are systematically selected for initial and continuing training.

4. Tasks/competencies are analysed to support development of training materials.

5. The plant specific task/competency inventory is clearly linked to training material to indicate the current supporting training programme content for each task/competency.

5. Design and development

Objectives: Training objectives that identify training content and define satisfactory trainee performance are derived from job performance requirements and feedback from operational experience.

Training materials are developed on the basis of training objectives.

Criteria: 1. Trainee entry level requirements are considered when developing training objectives.

2. Training objectives are developed and maintained current to establish the essential training content, the desired progression of learning, and the expected standards of trainee performance.

3. Training objectives are sequenced and grouped appropriately.

4. Test items, whether administered in a written, oral, job performance measure, or in a simulation format, are developed to measure effectively the required job related trainee KSAs/competencies, including higher level cognitive abilities such as analysis and diagnosis.

5. Lesson plans, laboratory guides, simulator lesson plans, job performance measures, individualized study guides, OJT guides, and other appropriate training materials are accurately developed and maintained to support training objectives and ensure quality and consistency in the conduct of training.

6. Valid examinations are developed and administered by using test items and pass/fail criteria to assess trainee KSAs.

6. Support of training with facilities, equipment and material

Objective: The training facilities, equipment and materials adequately support training needs.

Criteria: 1. Training facilities and equipment including simulators meet current training needs and are adequately maintained.

2. Plant laboratories and workshops used for training purposes adequately support training activities.

3. The training staff has necessary training aids and equipment.

4. Technical reference materials, including plant procedures and drawings, are current and readily available to trainees and instructors.

5. Models, mock-ups, and part task training simulators are representative of the actual unit/plant.

7. Conduct of classroom and individualized instruction and trainee assessment

Objective: Classroom and individualized instruction is presented effectively, and trainee performance is assessed consistently and reliably.

Criteria: 1. Training is implemented as outlined by approved training materials which are well organized and current.

2. Training activities encourage direct trainee participation in the learning process.

3. Instructors prepare adequately to ensure effective and consistent delivery of instruction.

4. Instructors use teaching techniques appropriate to the training objectives and lesson content.

5. When individualized instruction is used, sufficient guidance and supporting materials are provided to achieve the training objectives.

6. Trainee mastery of training objectives is assessed regularly by using written and/or oral examinations and tests.

7. Written and oral examinations and tests are administered and graded in a consistent manner.

8. Acceptance criteria to be used during the administration of oral examinations are defined in advance of the examination.

9. Remedial training and reassessment are provided when performance standards are not met satisfactorily.

8. Conduct of on the job training and trainee assessment

Objective: On the job training (OJT) is presented effectively, and trainee performance is assessed consistently and reliably to ensure that required job related skills and knowledge are possessed by trainees before their independent job and task assignment.

Criteria:

1. OJT is delivered by using approved training materials which are well organized and current.

2. OJT is conducted only by designated individuals who are qualified to perform the job and who can provide consistent and effective training and assessment.

3. The OJT programme is implemented by using a planned and logical instructional sequence.

4. When the task cannot be performed but is simulated or walked through, the conditions of task performance, references, tools, and equipment reflect the actual task.

5. Instructors use appropriate teaching techniques for the OJT being conducted.

6. Assessment of trainee performance is conducted by using established criteria to ensure that the trainee has obtained the essential knowledge and performance skills associated with the job and task before independent job and task assignment; the assessment is conducted by a qualified independent assessor.

7. Remedial training and reassessment are provided when performance standards are not met satisfactorily.

9. Conduct of simulator training for operating personnel and trainee assessment

Objective: Simulator training is presented effectively, and trainee performance is assessed consistently and reliably.

Criteria:

1. A suitable simulator, representative of the power plant control room, is used for hands-on training, to demonstrate operational characteristics, and for recognition and control of normal, abnormal and emergency conditions.

2. If simulator training is conducted on other than a plant referenced simulator, the training is adapted to the trainees' home plant.

3. Contracted simulator training is conducted with NPP approved training materials and is monitored by utility training personnel to ensure that trainees are achieving the specified training objectives. Contracted training should require vendor instructors to be familiar with differences between the simulator and the trainees' home unit/plant.

4. Differences between the simulator and the plant are reviewed with the trainees before training sessions.

5. Procedures used in the trainee's unit/plant are used whenever possible during simulator training.

6. Simulator training activities effectively strengthen diagnostic and teamwork skills.

7. Training is enhanced by the use of pre-exercise briefs, post-exercise critiques, and self-assessments. Post-exercise critiques and self-assessments reinforce strengths and identify and correct weaknesses in individual and team performance.

8. The plant's guidance for conduct of operations is effectively reinforced during simulator training activities.

9. Simulator training is implemented as outlined by approved training materials and is well organized and current.

10. Instructors prepare adequately for simulator sessions to ensure effective and consistent delivery of training.

11. The instructors use appropriate teaching techniques for the exercise being conducted.

12. Individual trainee and team performance are assessed regularly by line management and training personnel against established objectives by using appropriate methods and performance criteria.

13. Remedial training and reassessment are provided when performance standards are not satisfactorily met.

10. Conduct of laboratory training and trainee assessment

Objective: Laboratory training is presented effectively, and trainee performance is assessed consistently and reliably.

Criteria:
1. Laboratory training is implemented as outlined by approved training materials and is well organized, current and structured to provide actual practical experience.

2. Conditions of task performance, references, tools and equipment reflect the actual job.

3. Training activities encourage direct trainee participation in the learning process.

4. Instructors prepare adequately to ensure effective and consistent delivery of instruction.

5. The instructors use teaching techniques appropriate to the learning objectives and lesson content.

6. Trainee performance is assessed against established training objectives by using appropriate assessment methods and performance criteria.

7. Contracted training is assessed to ensure that trainees are achieving the specified training objectives.

8. Remedial training and reassessment are provided when performance standards are not met satisfactorily.

11. Feedback through a systematic evaluation of training effectiveness

Objectives: The systematic evaluation of training completeness and effectiveness is implemented effectively.

Evaluation results are used both for training programme improvements and plant improvements.

Criteria:
1. Input from supervisors, managers, trainers, trainees, and job incumbents is used to evaluate and improve training programmes.

2. The conduct of training is monitored and evaluated regularly in all settings.

3. Trainee performance assessed during training is used to evaluate and improve training programmes.

4. Changes such as regulatory changes, changes in job scope, results of external evaluations and inspections, changes in relevant industry documents, changes in procedures, plant systems, and equipment, similar unit/plant experience, results of root cause analysis, equipment and personnel performance trends, and industry experience are evaluated for applicability to initial and continuing training programmes.

5. Improvements and changes to initial and continuing training are systematically initiated, monitored and incorporated in a timely manner.

6. Evaluations of individual training programmes are conducted on a continuing or periodic basis to identify programme strengths and weaknesses.

7. Contracted training is evaluated for its contribution to meeting job performance requirements and to ensure that its quality is consistent with training standards.

10. SAT APPLICATIONS

The purpose of this section is to provide examples of the structure and content of training programmes for NPP staff judged to require high priority consideration by operating organizations for SAT implementation. The information provided in this section is mainly based on lessons learned from the use of SAT in the development and implementation of training programmes for NPP personnel. The content and structure of each of the sections are based upon the points important to that particular topic.

10.1. OPERATING PERSONNEL TRAINING

The aim of operating personnel training programmes is to obtain personnel qualified to operate a nuclear reactor and its auxiliary systems and equipment and to supervise those activities to ensure that they are performed in accordance with NPP policies, procedures, industrial safety practices and with applicable regulations. Errors of negligence by operating personnel in the execution of their task may result in catastrophic consequences for the plant, for the plant personnel and for the public at large. As a consequence, their training and qualifications assume a particular importance for the safety of the plant and its operation.

10.1.1. Operating personnel functions and responsibilities

To define the training and the qualification requirements for operating personnel, one must first define the functional responsibilities associated with their positions. In a typical NPP, these responsibilities are assigned as follows:

- **Shift supervisor**. The shift supervisor is responsible for the plant during a shift. This includes supervision of all operations in accordance with specified regulations and procedures and the co-ordination of all maintenance activities.
- **Control room operators**. Control room operators are responsible for monitoring the performance of all plant systems, operating controls in the control room according to operating procedures and directing operations on systems and equipment performed by field operators.
- **Field operators**. Field operators operate systems and equipment in the field according to operating procedures and instructions.

The position of shift supervisor requires intellectual skills at the level of evaluation. Since the time that is available to make decisions may be constrained by the requirements of plant operation, the shift supervisor's knowledge of the plant and procedures must be both broad and profound. Insofar as the duties of operators are to follow procedures or to follow the directions of the shift supervisor when procedures are not available, intellectual skills at the application level are adequate for operators, but their knowledge of the plant must be extensive. However, technical communication between the shift supervisor and the operators is facilitated if the operators have the intellectual skills and knowledge of the technology and the plant which are close to those of the shift supervisor, rather than having the minimum skills required if their tasks were simply to follow procedures and directions.

In general, the training requirements for unique or specialized KSAs for operating personnel cannot be met by sources outside NPPs and operating organizations. Therefore, it is common practice to recruit personnel directly from schools, technical colleges and universities, and to provide specialized theoretical training, on the job training, specific system and equipment training and simulator training at the NPP or other training organizations.

10.1.2. Design and development of training programmes

Sound training programmes for operating personnel are particularly important because of the impact that poorly trained operators could have on the plant, plant personnel and the public at large. This section, however, is not intended to provide general guidelines for the development of those programmes. Rather, the emphasis is on training in areas that may be somewhat underestimated when developing training for operating personnel.

10.1.2.1. Emergency response training

Training for accident response and management is an essential component of operating personnel training. There are a number of emergency oriented operations which should be subject to exercises but cannot be efficiently trained by simulation. As a consequence, in-plant exercises must be used to learn the practical aspects of emergency response and to practice manual skills. Operating personnel will normally train with other personnel for this type of training. Those exercises should include:

- Fire fighting exercises. These exercises must include both the handling of fire fighting and oxygen mask equipment and the practicing of alarm procedures with other plant departments and local fire departments. These exercises may also include first aid exercises.
- Emergency plant exercises. These exercises should include the handling of radiation monitoring and protection equipment as well as the practicing of alarm procedures for the case of internal or external radioactivity releases. These exercises should involve the participation of internal and external support groups.
- Handling of plant equipment that has to be activated in case of emergencies within a certain time period. These exercises may well be combined with surveillance tests.
- Evacuation of the control room following a fire or release of toxic gases. Plant shutdown from outside the control room.
- Unexpected plant conditions caused by the failure of remote systems, control devices, etc.

Plant exercises can be executed on an individual or on a team basis. The sequence of each exercise should be defined by scenarios and applicable procedures. The scenarios must reflect realistic plant conditions and should be based on case studies using simulation whenever possible, with the aim of minimizing the probability of operator error during an actual emergency. Training can be conducted via walkthroughs, by having the trainee observe actions in emergencies and by handling simulated plant emergencies.

Plant exercise scenarios, as with simulator scenarios, should be carefully prepared to include training objectives, terminating conditions and references. Furthermore, the conduct of a plant exercise should not create any condition which could jeopardize plant safety.

10.1.2.2. Emergency operating procedure training

Comprehensive training programmes must be provided to ensure that all operating personnel fully understand, and are familiar with, their plant operating procedures, especially for emergency conditions. A well designed emergency operating procedure (EOP) training programme, if properly implemented, will ensure that operating personnel have a good understanding of the conceptual basis of the EOPs, the terminology and structure of the EOPs, their roles and responsibilities during the execution of the EOPs and, last but not least, actual use of the EOPs. In-depth training on EOPs is especially important to overcome the degradation of operating personnel performance that can occur during stressful situations. Specific training is needed to ensure that EOPs usage, including terminology and format, is sufficiently understood so that plant personnel will interpret the EOPs consistently and correctly. Since specific effects of stress on an individual's performance cannot be accurately predicted, operator trainees must have an in-depth understanding of, and familiarity with, what the procedures look like and how they work. This will increase the likelihood that all operating personnel will execute the procedures correctly.

Training on EOP implementation should include, but is not limited to:

- A description of plant response to various types of initiating events using graphic examples as required. The description should be based on best estimate calculations or on actual operating data. A few alternatives of each type of event would be helpful and should show how the plant is brought to a safe shutdown state by controlling the symptoms.
- A discussion of the basic recovery strategy for each type of event and its possible alternatives. Results of calculations, as well as limiting conditions and constraints involved in the alternative strategies, must be given.
- An explanation of the principles of assuring plant safety by maintaining a set of critical safety functions.
- An explanation of the logic and organization of the procedure package including the roles of individual members of the operating team.
- A description of recovery methods and a discussion of the purpose of each step, or group of related steps, in the procedure.
- An explanation of the conditions and requirements under which a procedure could be modified including the required reference to, or possible changes in, the technical document.

An important component of EOP training is training on a full scope, plant specific control room simulator. Although simulators are a powerful tool in ensuring that operating procedures are properly understood, care should be taken to avoid that operators become too dependent on computer assistance. It is also important to train operators to develop and maintain their individual diagnostic capabilities. This enables them to recognize departures from normal operating conditions and the underlying causes for such departures.

Recent developments in symptom, function and state based procedures allow coverage of all analysed plant states in the event of departure from normal operating conditions and enable operators to take remedial action to avoid core degradation. These procedures may be used in conjunction with event oriented procedures after an abnormal event has occurred. In all cases, one of the important training objectives is timely intervention. Such intervention should be based on symptom, function and state based procedures and added into ongoing actions following event oriented procedures when the initial event diagnosis proves to be incorrect.

10.1.2.3. Team skills training

For most activities of operating personnel in a nuclear power plant there are attitudes and methods of working that are very important and that can be developed by training. Among the most important attitudes are discipline in following instructions and procedures and attitudes towards superiors and subordinates. Discipline can be developed by stressing the importance of training and by insistence on following correct procedures during practical exercises in training workshops and during supervised practice in the plant. All supervisory personnel are expected to demonstrate leadership in carrying out their responsibilities. One of the key aspects of a supervisor's relationship with those he supervises is communication, that is, passing all relevant information correctly and completely either up or down the organizational structure at the appropriate time. Training in communication within the organization can help to foster constructive, co-operative relationships within and among plant departments.

For most activities in the operation of an NPP, teamwork is important. The activities of each shift member are related to the operation of the plant, and the plant requires correct operator intervention at all times. Shift work calls for a much greater interdependence of operating personnel than any other area of nuclear power plant operation. The fact that the number of personnel on each shift is small and that the same people normally remain together for a considerable period of time emphasizes the team nature of the work.

Teamwork requires that individual tasks and responsibilities be assigned. By being aware not only of their own tasks and responsibilities but also of those of their colleagues, team members can lend each other mutual support. By having a thorough knowledge of the plant, they can make useful contributions to the resolution of abnormal situations. Successful teamwork also requires discipline. Teamwork can be improved through training. An especially useful opportunity is afforded during simulator training, but guided on the job training in the plant can also be structured to develop teamwork.

10.1.2.4. Cognitive skills training

A skill of critical importance for plant operating personnel is the ability to perform a correct process of evaluation and decision making in complex and unfamiliar situations, particularly under stress. Evaluation and decision making can be described as the set of activities required to select an appropriate action in an operational context. This definition includes everything from the initial indication that action is required through actual execution of the actions and, eventually, acting on the result-ing plant response. For the vast majority of cases in NPP operations, detailed proce-dures exist to guide the operator in the selection of actions.

However, despite the fact that operating organizations upgrade, refine and validate those procedures to maintain them at a high level of accuracy and completeness, there is growing evidence that procedures may not provide all of what is needed for the safe operation of the plant under abnormal and emergency conditions. The two main reasons for this are: the procedures may not contain sufficiently detailed guidance for certain control actions; and it is very difficult to control and update procedures to remove all errors. Another concern is certain types of situation that are so complex that they cannot be addressed properly in a procedure. These are the types of situation that have contributed to nuclear power plant incidents.

Even the shift from event based procedures to symptom based procedures, that is, from a requirement to diagnose and understand the current plant state (i.e. faults, system failures, etc.) to a situation where the operator is required to monitor a hand-ful of critical safety functions, or parameters, does not guarantee correct operator action during all possible plant upsets. For these reasons, operating personnel and other technical staff should rely not only on procedures but also on their own reason-ing about the state of the plant and the set of control actions that are appropriate. In other words, there is a need for operating personnel to develop cognitive skills that supplement procedures and provide a diverse redundant monitoring capability. Training programmes for operating personnel should endeavour to develop the abili-ty to produce solutions in unfamiliar situations under stress. Training on a simulator is particularly suitable to develop this ability using well designed scenarios that create situations requiring knowledge based evaluation and decision making.

10.1.3. Continuing training

A person's competence, once established, will in general increase with experi-ence but may also deteriorate with time. In particular, knowledge and skills which are seldom used may be forgotten. Similarly, the ability to act in situations that rarely occur or to perform activities that are practiced irregularly or at relatively long inter-vals may deteriorate. The competence required for a position may also change with time because of changes in plant hardware, operating methods, procedures and regu-lations. Since operations staff have the most direct impact on safe and reliable plant operation, their continuing training programme has to be reviewed on a regular basis to ensure that the programme content addresses actual needs. The various tasks of these personnel can be analysed with a high degree of accuracy based on the operat-ing procedures, observed performance discrepancies from plant operation, simulator training and reported incidents.

On the basis of the analysis phase of SAT, initial training topics should be reviewed to determine which tasks and their associated KSAs should be included in the continuing training programme. The following guidelines can help in selecting continuing training topics:

- Science and engineering fundamentals (e.g. applied thermodynamics, fluid dynamics, reactor physics and kinetics) should be reviewed at regular intervals for reactor operators and shift supervisors owing to the limited use of this knowledge in day to day operation. This review, when performed in conjunction with plant system training and simulator training, is useful in maintaining and improving diagnostic capability and cognitive skills (analysis, synthesis and evaluation).
- Operational procedures which are rarely used (abnormal and emergency procedures) should be reviewed periodically. It may also be beneficial to include some infrequently used normal operating procedures (e.g. plant startup) if these procedures have not been used recently or if improvement in operating performance is required.
- Topics covered in general employee initial training. This includes personnel safety, radiological protection, site regulations, emergency arrangements, fire protection and first aid.
- Severe accident management. The procedures to be followed in the event of a severe accident should be reviewed and practiced on a regular basis. These exercises are particularly useful to help operations staff to maintain a high level of competence in the areas of team work, communication and performance under stress.

A systematic review of recent operational experience and staff performance at the plant should also be included in continuing training. This should involve discussion on performance discrepancies and their causes. The review should also take into account deficiencies identified by quality assurance and quality control audits. Review of operational experience at similar plants through the use of incident reporting systems can be used to identify topics for inclusion in continuing training. All operating organizations should have in place a formal system for receiving and reviewing reports from other plants and for directing reports to the appropriate plant department and to their training departments.

Improving the preparedness of NPP personnel for scheduled operations and maintenance should also be considered part of a well designed continuing training programme. In this case, however, planning of the training should be done on an ad hoc basis and delivered just before these activities take place.

Finally, since the job functions of operating personnel are similar in many plants, review of continuing training programmes of other plants can be useful in defining the requirements of these programmes for one's own plant.

There is an emerging trend among operating organizations to follow a SAT approach in structuring continuing training programmes. This approach would start with an analysis phase where individual continuing training needs are identified by managers and supervisors. The identification is based on a review of the participation of the individuals in job related activities and an assessment of their performance during the execution of these activities. The analysis may include, where required, one or more tests to identify areas of knowledge where refresher training is appropriate. An appropriate training programme can then be structured on an individual basis.

Furthermore, it is well known that the motivation of plant personnel to participate in training sessions diminishes as time goes by. Participants in continuing training sessions are in general more critical than those undergoing initial training and will tend to evaluate their training needs in terms of job relevance and improvement of job performance, which is a valuable input in designing continuing training programmes. Individualized continuing training can provide this motivation.

10.2. MAINTENANCE TRAINING

10.2.1. Aims of training programmes for maintenance personnel

Section 10.2 deals among other things with training policy and sets out the goals and requirements of the development of training programmes. The aim is to obtain qualified personnel competent to perform all activities which are important for safety in nuclear power plants, in both operation and maintenance.

Statistically, in view of the great number of tasks, it can be said that a significant number of incidents are related to equipment or human factors problems associated with maintenance. The fundamental causes may be linked with the execution of job tasks, the maintenance documents used, the replacement parts or tools used, etc. They may also be due to inadequate training of maintenance personnel or to negligence or inadequacies in refreshing their competencies.

For this reason the training of maintenance personnel requires great care. To guarantee a high level of safety and availability of units, safety culture must be instilled and maintained. All personnel must appreciate the importance of maintenance for safety, so that greater care is applied to job tasks and the questioning attitude is sharpened.

The SAT methodology for maintenance personnel training fits in well with this context and these requirements, as it leads to the development of training programmes based on needs and competencies.

While this section does not describe in detail how training programmes for maintenance personnel are drawn up, it does provide lessons learned with respect to SAT based training programmes for maintenance jobs.

10.2.2. Analysis of maintenance training needs

Maintenance activities cover a broad scope and are carried out by personnel belonging to a number of NPP organizational departments. The organizational structure for maintenance stems from the history of the operating organization and its size, the local or national industrial infrastructure and, in some cases, governmental choices guided by the strategic energy considerations, as well as a number of other factors. Some operating organizations, for example, carry out all maintenance activities using their own personnel, while others subcontract practically all maintenance to the vendor or to other outside contractors. NPPs throughout the world choose the organization of maintenance activities in various ways, depending on the policy of the operating organization and, more specifically, its subcontracting policy.

Whatever the type of arrangement selected, the safety of NPPs is the operating organization's responsibility. With regard to maintenance activities and how these activities are carried out (by operating organization/NPP personnel or by subcontractors), the manner in which the responsibility is met varies.

Similarly, the level of qualification required of personnel working on maintenance activities must be adapted according to the complexity of the task to be executed, possible safety consequences, and the system of monitoring, evaluation and control. In general, qualification requirements concern only personnel working directly at NPPs and hence on-site.

10.2.2.1. Analysis of maintenance activities and associated competencies

To clearly determine the level of qualification required of maintenance personnel, quality related and safety related maintenance activities must be defined. The competencies (defined earlier to be groups of related KSAs) necessary to carry out these activities can then be established.

An analysis of maintenance activities for the various technical areas shows that there are two general types of competency:

- **Technical and professional competencies** to carry out correctly technical job tasks.
- **Human factors competencies** including those associated with risk management (see Section 5.8), which enable the activity to be carried out consistent with safety, thus controlling the consequences for the NPP and maintenance personnel.

These maintenance competencies can also be classified in the following three areas:

- Technical competencies concerning the NPP and its operation, the main objectives of which are related to:
  — General layout of the NPP.
  — Part of the NPP in which the task or activity is to be carried out.
- QA competencies, the main objectives of which are related to:
  — General procedures and rules applicable to the specific job.
  — QA rules and their application in job situations.
- Safety related competencies, the main objectives of which are related to:
  — Awareness of the consequences of job related actions for NPP safety.
  — Acquiring the safety culture common to all NPP jobs.

The lists of competencies are usually drawn up by subject matter experts/specialists on the basis of the activities and tasks to be carried out in the NPPs. Section 5 describes some of the main approaches used to analyse job related training needs and associated competencies.

10.2.2.2. Analysis of maintenance jobs

The competencies required for each job are derived from the activities which are to be performed in the job. In general, an individual's competence must be assessed before he/she can be entrusted with the activities and tasks concerned.

Whatever the **specialty** of a person with maintenance responsibilities (electrical, mechanical, instrumentation etc.), there are several **levels** of responsibility. For example, the activities entrusted to a person may be simple tasks carried out under the responsibility of a foreman or team leader, or complex tasks carried out alone. Similarly, different levels of qualification are required when the activity involves supervising a team.

The **functions** of a maintenance job may also vary on a temporary or permanent basis within a specialty, with different competencies required depending on whether the job involves simple task performance, work monitoring, work preparation or engineering functions.

The classification of maintenance jobs in accordance with the three criteria set out above (specialties, levels, functions) allows:

- Development of individual skills and therefore development in the job;
- Transfers within the various specialties;
- Development of training programmes and creation of multispecialty training modules.

10.2.3. Design of training programmes

10.2.3.1. Initial training

Initial training of maintenance personnel is broken down into several stages. The first three stages may be common to all jobs, while the later stages are more specifically adapted to jobs where risks associated with NPP operations and maintenance are involved.

- **Acquiring specialty related theoretical bases (mechanical, electrical etc.).** Maintenance personnel generally acquire knowledge from the national education system or the operating organization's/NPP's training programme either before employment or during in-service training.
- **Practical training on equipment to be maintained.** Such training is usually carried out by the manufacturers of the equipment concerned or by the operating organization/NPP. This training may be provided in the plant, at its training centre or at the manufacturer's facility. The choice often depends upon economic considerations or the manufacturer willingness/ability to provide training.
- **Risk prevention training, and training in industrial safety of staff and equipment.** All nuclear power plant personnel are involved in this training. As a result, it is usually carried out on site or at nuclear training centres by specialists and is used, in particular, to explain the emergency organization and the fire prevention equipment employed in the NPP.
- **Nuclear safety and QA training**. Classroom training with awareness enhancing training aids is used to train personnel in the basics of quality and safety. Safety concepts adapted to maintenance activities may be developed during practical training on the equipment. Through this training, human factors competencies can be developed related to: diagnostic abilities, risk analysis, teamwork, human system interface, questioning attitude, alertness, communication, organization, responsibility and management competence. Multispecialty training which reproduces the activities of the NPP is used to promote understanding of safety related factors.
- **Plant knowledge training.** For maintenance personnel, training in this area is carried out in the classroom with the aid of models. It often includes plant walkthroughs to show students the location of equipment. The teaching skills of the trainer are important for explaining clearly and simply the role of the principal equipment and the operation of the nuclear power plant. This training is used, in particular, to facilitate communications between the maintenance and operating teams.
- **Radiation protection training.** As with risk prevention training, all maintenance personnel are involved in this training, which is generally carried out on site by specialists. This training teaches radiation safety principles and the use of radiation protection equipment.

- **Training on emergency planning.** This training is usually carried out by means of a general classroom presentation of the on-site emergency plan and drills involving the various teams. The analysis and evaluation of such drills are an essential part of operational experience feedback, which helps improve performance.

10.2.3.2. Continuing training for maintenance personnel

In general, for maintenance activities, technical skills are maintained by being used on the job. However, effective use of resources may lead to a small number of people acquiring a specific qualification, either because the task is infrequently performed, or because it requires particular skills which are acquired through expensive or highly specific training. This is the case, for example, for some plant computers, where training is limited to a small number of specialists.

Others tasks which are infrequently performed can be scheduled well in advance, such as preventive maintenance. There is a cost effective alternative to providing both initial training and periodic continuing training. This is often referred to as 'just in time' training. Those tasks selected for 'just in time' training are not included in the initial training programme. Rather, specific training on performing these tasks is included in the schedule for performing the tasks, and is provided just before performing the tasks (i.e. weeks or days before performing the work). Just in time training can be considered part of continuing training — where the training schedule is determined by the related work schedule.

For each job, a training programme has been drawn up for the purpose of maintaining competence. Such training is used to revise and/or introduce:

- Revision of important initial training;
- New techniques or technologies;
- New equipment;
- New procedures;
- New regulatory requirements;
- New incidents which have occurred in the relevant area.

The programme is also used for experience feedback relating to both the content and the training process (trainers, training methods etc.); the use of new examples updates and lends credibility to the training.

Each of the maintenance personnel must have his job periodically evaluated by management. The observations arising from this may be used by management to draw up, together with the individual staff member, a list of specific training requirements. The training must meet NPP requirements, particularly those needed to make up for deficiencies observed during the performance of maintenance activities and tasks.

10.2.4. Development of training programmes

Competence consists of the ability to acquire, select and put into practice a given range of competencies. It can generally be observed in action. Line management carries out such observations to evaluate whether a maintenance staff member has the competence necessary for a particular job or activity.

Competencies may be acquired in several different ways, selected on the basis of cost and efficiency. The following distinctions are made:

- Training which provides knowledge on the basis of which skills can be developed. Such training is generally carried out in the classroom or laboratory,
- Training in techniques, used for acquiring skills directly. This type of training can be carried out on models or on equipment which is identical to that in NPPs, or by means of periods spent in operating conditions, shadow training, on the job training, workshop training, etc.

Safety culture can and should be instilled effectively in all safety related activities. The more important the action or activity is in terms of safety, the more efficiency is required of the training process and the resources (tools, materials, etc.) used in order to avoid errors, omissions and poor methods. These resources will also benefit from being as realistic as possible, both as regards the reproduction of equipment and its general environment.

Training using a model to simulate actual equipment, and training on a mock-up which reproduces identical working conditions, enables personnel to be confronted with situations as complex as those encountered in actual operation, and to acquire the necessary precision in their actions, particularly in a contaminated medium (e.g. steam generator water chamber, primary pump).

This type of training, which is well established in the field of welding, requires development in a number of other areas in which irreversible operations are carried out (such as plugging of steam generator tubes). Procedures must be validated and maintenance personnel must be qualified to ensure success at the first attempt. Such training, often carried out on copies which are identical with those installed in the controlled area, may take place on site, at the manufacturer's premises, or at a training centre.

Training on a mock-up where complex situations are reproduced (such as difficulties of technique, access, or radiation exposure) may also be used to recreate past incidents. The reaction capabilities of maintenance personnel in such situations, and the lessons learned through experience can thus be evaluated. Such training can be used to develop and improve technical and human factors competencies.

10.2.5. Implementation of maintenance training programmes

Training of maintenance personnel can be carried out at manufacturers facilities, which have the necessary technical skills and equipment. In such cases, the manufacturer acts as a training organization.

Training at manufacturers' premises must have the same quality guarantees as training carried out by the NPP and must be under the NPP's full control to allow information collection on personnel competence. This means that the required level and standards of performance expected from the implementation of this training must be precisely defined and closely monitored.

For each training programme it is necessary to define:

- The training objectives;
- Guidelines for trainers;
- Resources to be used;
- The system of assessment;
- The way in which nuclear and industrial safety and experience feedback are incorporated.

The reciprocal commitments between the NPP/operating organization and the training organization should be formalized through an agreement. This agreement should specify the way in which the plant management exercises quality control over the training provided, ensuring that the training objectives are met, including those related to safety culture.

Trainers working for the training organization should participate in actual maintenance activities on equipment in NPPs in order to maintain and update their competencies.

10.2.6. Evaluation of maintenance training programmes

All types of training activity which contribute to the acquiring of job related competencies must be evaluated and recorded, for QA and other purposes, whether these activities take place at the NPP or at an external training organization.

Evaluation and follow-up of training activities allow management to measure improvements in performance. Training effectiveness is demonstrated by improvements in job performance, such as:

- The proportion of activities carried out in the area in which the training is provided in comparison with the total operational activities of the trainees (for example, an electrician may devote only 20% of his work time to working on a particular piece of equipment).
- The qualifications of the trainees compared with the qualifications required for the job.

The important role of management in evaluating newly acquired competencies should also be stressed. Evaluation must:

- Enable managers to evaluate the job related technical and human factors competencies of individuals. In general, managers base their evaluation on the results of the training assessment, the job related experience acquired, and the capacity to assume professional responsibilities in the different situations encountered.
- Enable the staff member to recognize that he/she possesses the competencies necessary to carry out his/her job, and that he/she is capable of assuming the responsibilities entrusted to him/her, along with the obligations which derive from them.

It is important to formalize the joint commitment between management and the staff member. In so doing, safety becomes a central concern and everybody must meet the responsibilities that this entails. The responsibilities entrusted to each staff member must be limited to the activities/tasks for which the necessary competencies have been acquired.

Criteria may be defined to evaluate training activities, for example:

- A **training efficiency criterion** enables an evaluation to be made of the level of learning. This criterion may be established using questionnaires. It is an interesting exercise to compare trainees' views with those of trainers.
- A **relevance criterion** enables trainees to evaluate, on the basis of a preset questionnaire, all the elements used during the training to achieve the training objectives.

In addition, periodic feedback meetings (usually on a yearly basis) can be planned between the plant management and the training organizations, with the aim of improving and updating training programmes. Summaries of training programmes and analyses of their contribution to the plant improvements should be drawn up for this purpose.

10.2.7. Training of maintenance contractor personnel

To comply fully with their responsibilities, operating organizations must provide guarantees, in particular to regulators and to the public. They must have at their disposal all the information which demonstrates the competence of NPP maintenance personnel, and maintenance contractor personnel.

As with NPP maintenance personnel, there are two general types of competencies/ KSAs to be acquired and required for maintenance contractor personnel:

- **Technical and professional competencies**. Maintenance contractors are responsible for the training and qualification of their personnel and must have all the information which demonstrates that the necessary competencies have been acquired. The international standard (ISO) can be used in this field. The operating organization only checks the maintenance contractors through the ISO certification if it exists, otherwise through quality assurance of the contractors.
- **Human factor related competencies (KSAs)** including those associated with risk management in the nuclear industry.

Maintenance contractors are also responsible for the training and qualification of their personnel who, however, do not have the necessary nuclear related competencies. A training organization through which maintenance contractors can fulfil this responsibility must be established.

In such a case, the operating organization will develop, in conjunction with its contractors, compulsory training in fields such as safety, quality assurance, plant knowledge, risk prevention and radiation protection.

The operating organization should audit periodically this training organization to ensure that training is maintained at a high level of quality, and that trainers maintain their technical and teaching competencies.

Maintenance contractor personnel and NPP maintenance personnel performing the same jobs must have the same minimum qualifications and competence in areas such as quality assurance, risk prevention and ALARA. This creates confidence in the performance of activities entrusted to maintenance contractors and leads to good relations between maintenance contractors and NPP personnel.

For example, in one operating organization, the whole training programme followed by contractor personnel is recorded in an NPP access book, or 'passport'. An individual's passport enables its holder to carry out maintenance work at various sites; it indicates the training received, the level of certification issued by the employer and the total dose received at the various sites. This passport is also used as a quality assurance tool because it enables site access to be controlled and is legally and contractually binding for the employer of the individual (the maintenance contractor).

10.3. MANAGEMENT TRAINING

10.3.1. Aims of management training

Good NPP management is essential for plant safety and reliability. The critical function of managers thus requires special emphasis on their competence. Within this context the training programmes for plant management should be determined in the same way as for operations and maintenance personnel — using SAT based analysis, design, development, implementation and evaluation.

Plant management includes the following:

- First line managers (leaders of basic teams), e.g. head of shift operations, head of chemistry, shift supervisors.
- Second line managers (section/department heads), e.g. head of operations department, head of maintenance department, training department manager.
- Site/plant managers.

First line managers (subdepartment managers, group leaders)

The role of this level of management is to lead basic teams within plant departments. Typical job titles are: head of shift operations, head of chemistry, head of core surveillance, and head of radiation protection. Among these managers especially shift supervisors and/or safety engineers need special management training because of their job related challenges in dealing with plant events.

Second line managers (department heads)

Department managers are in charge of a number of specialized teams (subdepartments) related to one of the main plant functions. Typical job titles for these managers are: head of operations department, head of maintenance department, head of mechanical engineering and head of training. Usually, there are four to six department managers for a single unit.

Site/plant managers

These managers have overall responsibility for safe NPP operation of one or more nuclear power units, including the competence of all NPP personnel.

10.3.2. Analysis of management training needs

10.3.2.1. Technical know-how

As with other NPP staff, a fundamental requirement for managers is to have technical competence, which includes having the complete understanding and application of a body of knowledge and experience related to an area of technology: such as mechanics, electricity, automation, chemistry, operation, etc. The required competencies must be defined which are related to the tasks of a manager. The use of SAT as described in Chapters 4 to 9 of this Guidebook is recommended to define specific training needs, in the same way as for other positions, and to design, develop, implement and evaluate the training programmes. For technical knowledge and skills training, the same methods and tools could often be used as for other plant staff. However, training programmes specifically tailored to management are sometimes recommended.

10.3.2.2. Widening the field of knowledge

A manager's knowledge must be wider than only the knowledge related to his/her specific tasks within the organization. He/she must know the technical and safety aspects of his/her colleagues' activities as well as the regulations in force. All management staff of NPPs therefore need basic knowledge of:

- Reactor physics and radiation protection;
- Reactor safety philosophy and principles, at least, for their plant types;
- Nuclear regulations and requirements;
- Industrial safety and fire protection regulations and principles;
- Plant specific regulations and requirements;
- QA principles.

10.3.2.3. Experience

For leading others, a minimum of experience in the field of a person's tasks is necessary. The statement: 'A professional is someone who succeeds perfectly in all that he does due to past experience' (Larousse dictionary) underlines the need for experience for/in managing others. Experience itself is not a classical definition of 'training', but within the scope of 'management training' it is an important part. A minimum requirement for experience to take over management duties is therefore often regulated by authorities, and the training programme or the job descriptions should define minimum/optimum experience for managers.

Depending on the managerial level, it is usual to have the following practical experience for managers:

- **First line managers.** One to three years experience in their field of responsibilities. For functions with particular safety significance (e.g. safety engineers or shift supervisors) more experience is recommended.
- **Second line managers.** Three to five years experience in their field of responsibilities.
- **Plant/site managers.** Five to ten years experience in various fields of NPP operations.

10.3.2.4. Human factors competencies

In addition to technical competencies, managing includes:

- Co-ordination of actions between individuals and groups;
- Human resources management;
- Motivating, empowering and developing people;
- Coaching and mobilizing staff to develop their problem solving capabilities;

116

- Ensuring effective communications;
- Monitoring subordinates' performance;
- Leading the process of change and improvement.

10.3.3. Design of manager training programmes

Initial training programmes for managers are typically part of long term career planning within the NPP or operating organization.

Management training is therefore provided throughout the period of the individual's career development, rather than as a short term module in preparation for a particular job. A SAT based management training programme facilitates the control, continuity and completeness of long term management training.

Special training programmes for human factors competencies and management techniques are helpful to prepare technical experts for managing positions. A wide range of management training programmes are available. These programmes should be designed, developed, implemented and evaluated in accordance with SAT. In addition to the SAT analysis output, national and/or company specific management approaches must be taken into consideration to define appropriate programmes.

10.3.4. Implementation of manager training programmes

The training of managers is mainly performed by external organizations.

The aims and objectives of the training, quality of trainers, resources and methods used must be fostered and be consistent with the nuclear and industrial safety. Therefore, training programmes offered by organizations with similar approaches, such as airlines, chemical industries, etc., may be suitable.

It is important that external trainers become familiar with the principles of nuclear power and with SAT before conducting management training.

10.3.5. Continuing training of managers

On the basis of the output of SAT analysis, a continuing training programme for managers must also be defined. More so than for other staff, managers often do not participate in continuing training owing to the burden of their daily tasks and responsibilities. Especially tasks infrequently performed but of importance to plant safety, e.g. emergency preparedness, must be trained in continuing training programmes. It should be part of the safety culture within a plant that managers fulfil their own requirements for continuing training.

The continuing training programme has to consider also training for human factors competencies. Not only the refreshing of basic knowledge but also the change of management philosophies, company structures and approaches, etc. require continuing training and improvements of training programmes through a continuous evaluation and feedback process.

10.4. EMERGENCY PREPAREDNESS TRAINING

10.4.1. Aims of emergency preparedness training programmes

Since actual emergencies involving a nuclear power plant may be expected to occur infrequently, if at all, emergency preparedness exercises provide the only realistic opportunity to train and evaluate plant staff and staff from outside emergency response organizations in confronting accident conditions, to cope with them and to maintain and improve the effectiveness of the response. Emergency preparedness exercises are a learning process that must be designed to ensure that plant staff and staff from other participating organizations possess the essential KSAs required for the accomplishment of non-routine tasks under stressful conditions. Exercises provide experience in collaboration between groups which normally may not work together. They must be structured to provide experience in working under conditions similar to those that may prevail during an accident.

Many operating organizations require that personnel are trained to manage and mitigate beyond design basis accidents (BDBAs). It is therefore necessary that emergency preparedness training addresses this problem for all staff, including control room operating personnel.

This section does not describe in detail the overall training programme that is needed to face emergency situations. Rather, it addresses issues related to SAT based emergency preparedness training programmes.

10.4.2. Analysis of tasks

Response to an emergency condition requires a broad range of activities that must be carried out by plant personnel and by personnel from outside organizations. Their specific duties and responsibilities vary and so does the level of qualification required of them. The following are examples of activities which need to be considered in the analysis of emergency preparedness training needs:

- Notification to national and international authorities in case of a transboundary accident.
- Initial response including accounting, assembly and safe evacuation of plant personnel.

- Radiological monitoring including availability of appropriate equipment for plant surveys, ingestion pathways monitoring, sample collection and analysis, data assessment and trend monitoring.
- Off-site exposure assessment including source term evaluation, meteorological data evaluation, projected dose evaluation, and correlation of in-plant and environmental data.
- Personnel dose assessment and control including dosimeter processing, exposure authorization and control, issuing work permits and specific radiation protection measures.
- Off-site protection measures including distribution of radioprotective prophylactic drugs, evacuation and sheltering procedures, traffic control, establishing evacuee reception centres, agricultural control.
- Medical services including first aid, screening of potentially exposed persons, treatment of contaminated or highly exposed individuals.
- Accident analysis including status of main safety systems and fission product barriers, accident classification, possible corrective actions or actions to mitigate release of radioactivity.
- Public information including prompt warning of the public, activating a public information centre, maintaining information to the public and prevention of public alarm.
- Administration including activating emergency control and co-ordination centres, record keeping, shift staffing, logistic support.
- On-site recovery measures including emergency rescue, fire fighting, use of respiratory protection equipment, access control to the affected plant and damage assessment and control.
- The management of BDBA.

10.4.3. Initial training programmes

Emergency preparedness exercises are training and evaluation tools that are necessary to provide plant staff with experience in implementing an emergency plan effectively. In addition to these exercises, supporting training is needed to prepare personnel to perform specialized emergency duties.

10.4.3.1. NPP personnel training

Some NPP personnel will have emergency assignments, such as emergency co-ordinators, accident assessment teams, radiological monitoring teams, fire brigades, first aid and rescue teams, chemistry sampling teams and off-site response teams. While NPP personnel emergency assignments will be based on their routine jobs assignments, there remains a need for them to receive specialized training relevant to the duties they will have to perform during an emergency. The purpose of this training is to:

- Demonstrate how effectively an emergency plan, or a section of it, can be implemented;
- Confirm the plan adequacy to deal with the emergency and to identify potential improvements;
- Verify that the appropriate lines of communication are established and maintained;
- Verify that all individuals participating in the exercise are familiar with, and capable of, performing the emergency duties assigned to them;

This training must address:

- The different segments of the emergency response plan;
- Related procedures such as those for health physics and emergency operations;
- Use of equipment.

Where appropriate, the training sessions should take into account any need for co-operation or co-ordination with other individuals and working groups having similar or complementary emergency duties (e.g. between fire, first aid and rescue groups).

Initial as well as continuing training for BDBA management may be conducted in a combination of settings including simulation, emergency drills and classroom. Control room simulators are usually not validated for BDBAs, and great care is required in their use for the training of operating personnel in BDBA. Other types of simulation may be considered. There is a trend to upgrade the models associated with all types of control room simulators to model a greater range of accidents. However, it must be stressed that the use of simulation for BDBA training is a new area, and little experience has been obtained to date.

10.4.3.2. NPP co-operation in public sector training

The participation of public authorities and news media during an emergency is an essential element in the protection of the public and in mitigating the effects of an accident. In addition to their decision making and information responsibilities during an emergency, public authorities and news media may also contribute to the response action. Their areas of involvement would include field monitoring, transportation and traffic control, communication and public information, assistance to members of the public including medical care and protection of property. Furthermore, national defense and government laboratories are often able to provide equipment and human resources to support public authorities. For these reasons, it is important that public sector emergency service staff be appropriately trained and familiar with the particular needs of nuclear emergency procedures.

Specifically, staff in the public sector as well as staff of the news media who might be required to present information to the public should be familiar with the emergency planning arrangements through periodic discussions with members of the operating organization and through visits to the NPP. They should also be informed on those matters that may be relevant to their participation in the event of a nuclear emergency, such as the basic principles of control of exposure to radiation or contamination, radiation protection and the operation of measuring instruments. The necessary training and familiarization should be facilitated by the operating organization. There may also be requirements for public sector service teams, such as local fire departments and ambulance teams to assist in an on-site emergency. Although the members of these teams may be expected to be proficient in their own particular skills, they may be unfamiliar with the layout of the plant and with the conditions that may prevail during an emergency, such as high radiation levels, escaping steam and toxic gases. The members of these teams should, therefore, train with NPP personnel so that they become accustomed to the potential adverse environmental conditions under which they may be required to work.

10.4.4. Assessing emergency preparedness exercises

During emergency preparedness exercises, personnel familiar with the emergency response being demonstrated, but without other duties during the exercise, should be assigned to observe and assess the performance of emergency response personnel. To provide constructive criticism, the assessors must have sufficient knowledge to able to follow and understand the emergency actions that are carried out by the personnel they are assessing. This requires that the assessors be either experienced emergency response personnel, or, if such individuals are not available, personnel with training and experience in the field to which they are assigned.

10.4.5. Continuing training

The frequency of continuing training sessions must take into account the nature and complexity of the particular tasks and the level of performance that must be maintained by each emergency response assignment. For example, individuals or groups concerned with rapid response duties such as fire fighters, rescue and off-site radiological monitoring may need to be provided practice sessions on a regular basis.

It is recommended that all personnel with responsibilities for implementing the emergency plan should attend appropriate continuing training sessions at least annually.

10.4.6. Evaluation of emergency preparedness training programmes

It is very important to use critiques from emergency preparedness exercises and feedback from other emergency preparedness training activities to improve the emergency preparedness training programme, the emergency plan, implementing procedures and equipment. For any deficiency revealed, whether in procedures, equipment or personnel performance, the root cause should be identified and appropriate corrective actions should be promptly taken.

10.5. INSTRUCTOR TRAINING

The quality of nuclear power plant personnel training is strongly dependent on the availability of competent instructors. Instructors must have a comprehensive practical as well as theoretical understanding of all aspects of the subjects being taught and the relationship of the subject to nuclear plant operation. Hence, it is preferable for instructors to have held a post at an NPP relevant to their field of teaching responsibility. For example, control room simulator instructors should have held a shift operations post at appropriate level of seniority in a plant of the same design.

It can be beneficial for the instructors in training organizations to consist of a mix of permanent and rotating staff. The rotating staff should be from NPPs served by the training organizations and should be assigned as full time trainers for periods of one to three years, and thus:

- Bring up to date experience into the training function;
- Provide feedback to the training programme;
- Add credibility, particularly with staff undergoing continuing training.

All instructors must have, or acquire through training, teaching KSAs needed to enhance training and learning. In addition, instructors should be trained in the use of SAT, particularly in the phases to which they contribute (it has been found beneficial for instructors to participate in all phases of SAT).

Teaching KSAs are also needed for part time instructors, including those who provide training in the plant. Training provided for these KSAs should be tailored to the particular training setting(s) for which the part time instructor will participate.

10.5.1. Instructor qualification

The operating organization should establish a formal programme for selecting, training and certifying instructors.

The selection criteria for instructors should include the required technical KSAs, based upon the subjects to be instructed and the future jobs of the trainees. In addition, candidates should demonstrate the following:

- Good attitude towards training;
- Excellent communication skills;
- Aptitude for instructing.

122

Instructors for simulator training of operating personnel

Not only must instructors for simulator training of operating personnel have experience in control room and other relevant operations, they must also have training in the operation of the simulator. This training should include both operation of the simulator and use of the simulator as a training and evaluation tool. The instructor must learn to operate the simulator (initialize, freeze, snapshot, etc.), to inject malfunctions, to understand the boundaries of validity of the simulator and to operate facilities used in support of the training session, e.g. video cameras, recording equipment. Unique aspects associated with simulator training which need to be included in the instructor training programme are those relevant to:

- Development of diagnostic skills;
- Teamwork within the shift;
- Introduction and management of stress on the trainee(s).

10.5.2. Establishing teaching competence

Most instructors need to acquire teaching competencies by completing a training programme designed for this purpose. Both initial and continuing training are needed to establish and maintain instructors' competence.

A training programme on the fundamentals of teaching would typically address the following competencies:

- Understanding the role of the instructor;
- Arranging the classroom (or other training setting) to fit training sessions;
- Understanding how adults learn;
- Using appropriate training techniques;
- Using lesson plans and training materials;
- Conducting lectures;
- Conducting discussions;
- Conducting practical demonstrations;
- Assisting trainees in solving problems associated with learning;
- Assessing trainees;
- Maintaining and using individual trainee records and training programme records;

An example of a training objective of fundamental instructional training might be as follows:

Given a prepared lesson plan, which includes appropriate training material, the instructor trainee should be able to deliver the lesson. This lesson should be consistent with the content of the training programme, and the teaching techniques should be appropriate for the setting, the training aids and the intended trainees.

To qualify for more advanced assignments, the instructor should demonstrate competence to carry out classroom training and should complete additional training, which may include:

- Designing training programmes;
- Planning and developing lessons;
- Developing lesson plans;
- Selecting, developing and modifying training materials;
- Developing instructional measurement methods;
- Presenting laboratory instruction;
- Managing individualized instruction;
- Conducting walkthroughs and station tours;
- Conducting simulator training;
- Supervising on the job training;
- Identifying trainee stress.

A training objective for advanced teaching skills training might be as follows:

Given training related information, the instructor trainee should be able to prepare a lesson plan that contains at least the following elements:

— Plant system and task (or competency);
— Training objectives;
— Training material and aids;
— Trainee assessment;
— Estimated time.

10.5.3. Certification of instructors

The plant training manager, or manager of the relevant training organization, in conjunction with other appropriate individuals, should certify that an instructor is technically qualified to present the material and has the teaching skills to perform training tasks as needed for a specific job position.

Certification of technical competence should be based upon a demonstration of the appropriate technical KSAs in the subject area(s) to be taught by the instructor. Certification of teaching KSAs should be based upon demonstrated performance of training tasks for the specific instructor position. The final certification of instructors should be based upon evaluating their performance through observation of a number of training sessions.

10.5.4. Continuing training programmes for instructors

Continuing training programmes should be established to maintain, improve and advance both the technical and teaching competence of qualified instructors. The continuing training programme for instructors should consist of two elements: technical training and teaching skills training:

10.5.4.1. Continuing technical training

The purpose of this training is to maintain technical qualification and familiarity with job requirements, plant changes, operational experience, plant documents, etc. Instructors should maintain their job qualification by fully participating in continuing training programmes in the area of expertise for which they are providing instruction. All instructors should periodically work in the plant in the discipline for which they are qualified and for which they prepare trainees. Some NPPs use time during scheduled plant outages for this purpose. In the case of simulator instructors, this in-plant time should be on shift to include plant activities such as shutdown and startup associated with refuelling outages. Many operating organizations periodically rotate technical instructors back to the plant and/or assign plant personnel to the training staff for extended periods (i.e. one to two years).

10.5.4.2. Continuing training for maintaining teaching competence

Continuing training for maintaining teaching KSAs aims at improving and advancing the instructors' teaching competence. The training consists of reviewing selected initial training topics, in-depth instruction on selected topics, information on new training methods and aids, information on changes in training related regulations or procedures, and observing and evaluating other instructors. The training content should also be based on feedback from assessments of instructors and evaluation of training programmes.

10.6. PROJECT MANAGEMENT TO INTRODUCE SAT BASED TRAINING

This section provides information based on experience to date on the introduction of SAT based training at NPPs in various countries.

For a SAT project whose goal is to upgrade existing training programmes or to establish new ones through the successful implementation of SAT, it is essential for the NPP and/or operating organization to provide the required resources: human, financial, administrative and technical support.

Quality assurance for SAT implementation must be established at the NPP. The NPP or operating organization must assign a project manager and must establish implementing procedures for all SAT phases, which must comply with the QA programme of the plant. It is also necessary to define the interrelationships among plant departments and between the plant and external organizations.

In some cases the NPP may not be able to start the project without external assistance, owing to insufficient knowledge and experience concerning SAT. It is thus highly recommended to engage at the beginning external experts who have already performed SAT based training at another NPP. The IAEA can also play an important role in the process of introducing and implementing SAT, particularly through its technical co-operation projects specifically addressing such purposes.

10.6.1. Role of NPP and operating organization management

To implement effectively a project on SAT based training, an NPP and the operating organization should:

- Have a strong commitment to the project.
- Be familiar with SAT and how it can contribute to enhancing NPP safety and reliability.
- Assume or assign the responsibilities as described in Section 2.3.2.
- Identify training needs for all jobs having an impact on plant safety and reliability. These training needs should be formally documented and approved by the plant manager or operating organization.
- Estimate and allocate sufficient resources to the project (human, financial, equipment and time).
- Assess the level and availability of supporting infrastructures (technical, educational, industrial).
- Approve the principal documents for the project (QA programme, project implementation plan, SAT implementing procedures).

10.6.2. Project management and support

- Select a project manager having the appropriate qualifications and competence;
- Develop a detailed project implementation plan, which must include project evaluation;
- Form a project team which includes, among others, those who are, or will become, qualified instructors;
- Promote the project;
- Engage, where needed, the necessary expertise for transferring and adapting the SAT methodology.

To support the project it will be necessary to provide, among other things, the following:

- Appropriate offices for the project team;
- Computer hardware and software appropriate to introducing SAT based training;
- Communication equipment.

126

10.6.3. Training of the project team

The project team will require some additional training which may consist of, but may not be limited, to:

- Understanding the basic principles of SAT.
- Visits to training centres and NPPs where SAT is used.
- Training in:
  — SAT methodology;
  — Use of SAT procedures;
  — Development of SAT based training materials.

10.6.4. Project implementation

The project implementation plan is based on the:

- Identification of training needs;
- Identification of jobs (or sets of related jobs) which the project will address, based on the identified training needs;
- Detailed plan and procedures for implementing SAT which has been adapted to the needs and conditions of the individual NPP and country.

11. IAEA ACTIVITIES AND TECHNICAL CO-OPERATION IN NPP PERSONNEL TRAINING AND QUALIFICATION

Department of Nuclear Energy, Department of Technical Co-operation, Department of Nuclear Safety

IAEA assistance to and co-operation with Member States in the area of nuclear power including NPP personnel training is provided primarily through the Department of Nuclear Energy, the Department of Technical Co-operation and the Department of Nuclear Safety. Technical co-operation should meet overall national goals related to safe, reliable nuclear power and should have a significant impact on, and relevance for, national nuclear power programme needs and priorities. The Department of Technical

127

Co-operation is responsible for all matters related to the programming and administrative implementation of projects and other assistance, while the Department of Nuclear Energy and the Department of Nuclear Safety are responsible for the technical aspects of assistance in NPP personnel training and qualification, including the technical implementation of projects.

The main objective of all activities of the IAEA in NPP personnel training is to increase a country's capability of providing qualified, competent NPP personnel through appropriate training. Technical co-operation projects and other assistance aim at introducing, improving or updating programmes and facilities associated with NPP personnel training, including relevant nuclear related education. Technical co-operation and requests for assistance are generally initiated by Member States through project proposals. Regional projects are usually proposed by the Department of Technical Co-operation. If a project is approved, there are various delivery mechanisms for project implementation which include expert missions, seminars, workshops, fellowships, scientific/technical visits, training courses (interregional, regional, national) and provision of equipment.

The Guidebook on Nuclear Power Plant Personnel Training and its Evaluation — and, in particular, SAT — represents the official Agency guidance and recommendations related to NPP personnel training and qualification, and is thus used in implementing Agency activities.

In the Department of Nuclear Energy, the programmes of the Division of Nuclear Power, in particular the Nuclear Power Engineering Section (NPES) of this Division, support the development of safe, reliable nuclear power including the transfer of knowledge and experience which enables individual countries and NPPs to provide SAT based training for attaining and maintaining the competence of NPP personnel. Project related and other assistance is provided not only in NPP personnel training and qualification using, but also in planning nuclear power programmes, NPP project management, QA, instrumentation and control and NPP maintenance. The NPES and other relevant technical sections/divisions of the Agency facilitate the transfer of knowledge and experience to Member States through: the development of publications (guidebooks, databases, standards); specialists meetings; co-ordinated research programmes; and the technical implementation of Technical Co-operation projects, missions and training courses.

Enhancing NPP personnel training capabilities and self-sufficiency is supported through activities of the Department of Nuclear Energy, the Department of Nuclear Safety and the Department of Technical Co-operation related to:

- Transfer of know-how and experience on the introduction and use of SAT to develop, implement and evaluate training programmes;
- Training courses;
- Upgrading education and training systems for professional and technician level personnel;

- Training of trainers;
- On the job training;
- Training advisory services;
- Training centre development;
- Upgrading of training related facilities;
- Provision of equipment;

in technical subject areas such as:

- Human resources development including SAT;
- Nuclear power and safety;
- QA;
- Radiation protection;
- Nuclear fuel cycle and waste management.

It is in the best interests of the receiving country/organization that there be accountability associated with technical co-operation and the provision of assistance, to ensure the most efficient and effective use of resources. Projects must be identified, designed and developed very carefully with evaluation and feedback built into them from the beginning. Thus, there must be clearly defined objectives and performance indicators to permit meaningful and regular evaluation during a project and at the end of a project, to determine whether the assistance has been provided in an effective, efficient manner and has had the intended impact.

OSART MISSIONS

The IAEA Operational Safety Review Team (OSART) programme provides, on request by a Member State, advice and assistance to enhance the safety of nuclear power plants during construction, commissioning and operation. The OSART programme, initiated in 1982, is not restricted to any particular group of Member States, whether developing or industrialized, but is available to all countries with NPPs under construction, commissioning or in operation.

The purpose of the OSART programme is to assist Member States in enhancing the operational safety of specific NPPs and to promote the continuous development of operational safety within all Member States by the dissemination of information on good practices.

OSARTs thus focus on the safety and reliability of plant operation. They review the operation of the plant and the performance of the plant's management and staff rather than the adequacy of a plant's design. Factors affecting plant management and the performance of personnel, such as organizational structure, management goals, and the qualification of personnel are reviewed. Adequacy of programmes and performance related to operational activities are given particular attention. Guidelines used by the teams to review plant programmes and performance are based on best international practices and are applied in light of the experience of the entire team.

Specifically, the OSART missions review the following aspects regarding the training and qualification of NPP personnel: training organization and functions/tasks; training programmes; training facilities, equipment and materials for: control room operators and shift supervisors, field operators, maintenance personnel, technical support personnel, radiation protection personnel, chemistry personnel, management and general employees.

OSART review teams generally use the IAEA Guidebook on Nuclear Power Plant Personnel Training and its Evaluation as the basis for evaluation of training and qualification programmes.

ASSET MISSIONS

The IAEA Assessment of Safety Significant Events Team (ASSET) service assists Member States by advising them on enhancing operational safety through an effective policy of prevention of incidents at NPPs. Although good design, manufacture and construction of an NPP are prerequisites, safety ultimately depends on the competence and qualifications of NPP personnel and on the professional attitude with which they carry out their duties. ASSET missions concentrate on these aspects in assessing the policy for the prevention of incidents against successful policies in other countries; and in exchanging, at the working level, ideas for improving policy.

An ASSET review is undertaken at the request of operating or regulatory organizations of a Member State but it is not a regulatory type of inspection to determine compliance with national requirements. An ASSET review can complement national efforts by providing an independent, international assessment which may identify areas for improvement that have been overlooked.

ASSET reviews are instrumental in identifying root causes related to human factors and their implications for training. Especially for root causes related to equipment failure, further analysis can yield a deeper human factors related root cause in many cases, and this requires feedback of the results of the deeper insights into the training process.

The final goal of an ASSET review is to provide conclusions on the appropriateness and completeness of the planned and implemented corrective actions. Generic lessons are drawn and suggestions are offered, when necessary, to improve plant management control on prevention of incidents, thus enhancing the overall level of operational safety.

GLOSSARY OF TERMS

assessment. A formal, structured process through which the knowledge, skills and attitudes of a trainee are measured. The process may be based on oral tests, written tests, simulator tests or job performance demonstrations.

assessor. An individual responsible for the assessment of trainees, who is fully qualified at, or above, the level to be attained by the trainee in the area to be assessed.

attitude. The personal feelings, perceptions, values and interests of an individual which allows a job or task to be undertaken to the best ability of that individual.

authorization. The granting of a written permission by the operating organization to perform the duties and responsibilities of a position based on demonstrated competence.

certification. Formal recognition of successful completion of training by a trainee following assessment.

competence. The ability to put skills and knowledge into practice in order to perform a job in an effective and efficient manner to an established standard.

competency. A group of related knowledge, skills and attitudes needed to perform a particular job.

enabling objective. (See **training objective**)

entry level requirements. The combination of education, training and experience required to enter a training module or training programme.

evaluation. (See **SAT evaluation phase**)

feedback. The input from the collection and analysis of evaluation data to improve nuclear power plant operations and training.

job. The duties and tasks performed by an individual.

job analysis. A systematic process for obtaining a detailed listing of the responsibilities, duties and tasks of the job.

job competencies analysis. The determination, by an expert group, of competencies which are needed to perform a job.

lesson plan. A detailed plan that outlines instructor and trainee activities, identifies training objectives and test items, lists the resources needed for its conduct and includes instructor material, trainee material and references.

licensing. The issuing of written permission by the regulatory body to an individual to perform specific activities related to the operation of a nuclear power plant.

management. The functional levels in the operating organization comprising those individuals assigned overall responsibility for the safe and reliable operations of the plant(s) including their administrative aspects.

mock-up. Models of equipment or systems used for training.

module plan. A structured set of lesson plans and a timetable for their use.

operating organization. The organization authorized by the regulatory body to operate the plant. In some instances the operating organization would be termed 'utility'.

operating personnel. Personnel involved in the direct operation of systems and equipment in the NPP. This group contains control room and field operators.

operation. All activities performed to achieve the purpose for which the NPP was built, including maintenance, refuelling, in-service inspection and other related activities.

operational experience. All experience concerned with the operation of an NPP, including incidents and accidents with root causes associated with any aspect of human performance including maintenance and other associated activities.

plant department manager. An individual who directs the activities of other personnel, performs tasks and discharges responsibilities, within a specific functional area.

plant manager. Individual who has been allocated responsibility and delegated authority by the operating organization for directing operations of the nuclear power plant(s).

plant training manager. An individual with allocated tasks and responsibilities relating to the co-ordination of all plant personnel training issues.

procedure (relating to SAT). Document containing guidance, personnel responsibilities and step by step instructions on how to perform the activities required to successfully implement each phase of SAT.

qualification. The combination of education, training and experience required to meet specified job performance criteria.

qualification programme. A set of compulsory training modules leading to qualification, certification or authorization to perform a job or specific activities.

safety culture. That assembly of characteristics and attitudes in organizations and individuals which establishes that, as an overriding priority, nuclear plant safety issues receive the attention warranted by their significance.

SAT analysis phase. The identification of the training needs and of the competencies required to perform a particular job.

SAT design phase. The conversion of competence requirements into training objectives and the production of a training plan.

SAT development phase. The preparation of all the training material to meet the training objectives.

SAT evaluation phase. The collection and collation of all data obtained, according to procedures, during each of the phases. This is followed by suitable actions to improve programme effectiveness.

SAT implementation phase. Conduct of training using procedures and the materials developed.

simulation. Setting up situations representing the work environment or conditions. Examples of simulation are: control room simulators, mock-ups, and case studies.

skill. The ability to perform a task to a specified standard.

subject matter expert. An individual qualified and experienced in performing a particular task, a set of tasks or highly knowledgeable in some specific subject area.

systematic approach to training (SAT). A logical progression from the identification of the competencies required to perform a job to the development and implementation of training to achieve these competencies, and subsequent evaluation of this training.

task. A defined work sequence, within a job, with identifiable start and end points. Physical or intellectual action to be carried out with an observable or measurable result.

task analysis. A systematic process for examining a task to identify the methods of correct performance and underlying competencies in terms of the required knowledge and skills.

task element. A step that must be undertaken as one of a sequence in order to complete a task.

terminal objective. (See **training objective**)

test. (See **assessment**)

trainer. A person, with the appropriate qualifications, who provides training. Examples of trainers are: a full time trainer (internal or external), and a part time trainer (plant personnel such as an experienced worker or supervisor).

training module. Integrated portion of training that forms part of a training programme. Each module is complete in itself. It is defined by training objectives, prerequisites, a duration and contents. A course is an example of a training module.

training needs analysis. The process which examines performance needs and deficiencies and identifies appropriate solutions.

training objective. Statement of what trainees will be able to do upon completion of a particular part of a training programme, to what standards and under what conditions. There are two types of training objectives, terminal and enabling. **Terminal objectives** are directly related to specific tasks/competencies and reflect trainee performance requirements upon completion of a training programme. **Enabling objectives** describe trainee KSAs that must be mastered before the terminal training objective can be accomplished.

training plan. A detailed plan, which is a product of the design phase, containing a list of training objectives, appropriate training settings, schedule of training modules, identification of modules relevant to more than one group of personnel, entry level requirements of trainees, test items and an estimate of the required resources.

training policy. A formal document issued by the operating organization containing the goals and scope of training, the organization and responsibilities for its implementation and the methods of monitoring and controlling its effectiveness.

training programme. Organized set of training modules and settings, with the purpose of meeting all the training objectives for a particular job.

training setting. The environment in which training is conducted. Examples of training settings include classroom, simulator, laboratory, workshop and self-study.

validation. The means by which a process is tested to ensure that it is usable, that the language and the level of information are appropriate for whom it is intended and that the process will function as intended.

LIST OF ABBREVIATIONS

ALARA	As low as reasonably achievable
ASSET	IAEA assessment of safety significant events team
CBT	Computer based training
EOP	Emergency operating procedure
I&C	Instrumentation and control
IAEA	International Atomic Energy Agency
JCA	Job competencies analysis
JTA	Job and task analysis
KSA	Knowledge, skill and/or attitude
NPP	Nuclear power plant
OJT	On the job training
OSART	IAEA operational safety review team
PWR	Pressurized water reactor
QA	Quality assurance
SAT	Systematic approach to training
SME	Subject matter expert
VDU	Visual display unit
WANO	World Association of Nuclear Operators

CONTRIBUTORS TO DRAFTING AND REVIEW*

Billard, P.	Electricité de France, France
Birnie, S.	Stuart Birnie Partnership, United Kingdom
Deffrennes, M.	European Commission, Belgium
Ducháč, A.	Nuclear Power Plant Jáslovske Bohunice, Slovak Republic
Eriksson, L.R.	Nuclear Training and Safety Center (KSU), Sweden
Farber, G.	Gesellschaft fur Anlagen- und Reaktorsicherheit (GRS) GmbH, Germany
Förster, K	Rheinisch-Westfälische Elektrizitätswerks AG, Germany
Grauf, E.	Gemeinschaftskernkraftwerk Neckar GmbH, Germany
Haber, S.B.	Brookhaven National Laboratory, United States of America
Iyo, N.	Nuclear Power Training Center, Japan
Kazennov, A.Yu.	ENIKO MIFI, Russian Federation
Kim, V.	GOSKOMATOM, Ukraine
Kiss, I.	Paks Nuclear Power Plant, Hungary
Kováč, P.	State Office for Nuclear Safety, Czech Republic
Mautner Markhof, F.	International Atomic Energy Agency
Mazour, T.	Mazour Associates, Inc., United States of America
Mendizabal, J.L.	Tecnatom S.A., Spain
Pianarosa, P.	Atomic Energy Control Board, Canada
Suh, In-Suk	Korea Atomic Energy Research Institute, Republic of Korea
Taylor, F.E.	Nuclear Installations Inspectorate, United Kingdom

---

* The affiliations given here are those that pertained at the time of the meetings.

Consultants Meetings

Vienna, Austria: 27 June–1 July 1994;
5–9 December 1994; 27–31 March 1995; 15–19 May 1995

Advisory Group Meeting

8–12 May 1995

HOW TO ORDER IAEA PUBLICATIONS

No. 2, January 1996

☆ ☆ **In the United States of America and Canada**, the exclusive sales agents for IAEA publications, to whom all orders and inquiries should be addressed, is:

UNIPUB, 4611-F Assembly Drive, Lanham, MD 20706-4391, USA

☆ ☆ **In the following countries** IAEA publications may be purchased from the sources listed below, or from major local booksellers. Payment may be made in local currency or with UNESCO coupons.

AUSTRALIA	Hunter Publications, 58A Gipps Street, Collingwood, Victoria 3066
BELGIUM	Jean de Lannoy, 202 Avenue du Roi, B-1060 Brussels
CHINA	IAEA Publications in Chinese:
	China Nuclear Energy Industry Corporation, Translation Section,
	P.O. Box 2103, Beijing
CZECH REPUBLIC	Artia Pegas Press Ltd., Palác Metro, Narodni tř. 25, P.O. Box 825,
	CZ-111 21 Prague 1
DENMARK	Munksgaard International Publishers Ltd., P.O. Box 2148,
	DK-1016 Copenhagen K
EGYPT	The Middle East Observer, 41 Sherif Street, Cairo
FRANCE	Office International de Documentation et Librairie, 48, rue Gay-Lussac,
	F-75240 Paris Cedex 05
GERMANY	UNO-Verlag, Vertriebs- und Verlags GmbH, Dag Hammarskjöld-Haus,
	Poppelsdorfer Allee 55, D-53115 Bonn
HUNGARY	Librotrade Ltd., Book Import, P.O. Box 126, H-1656 Budapest
INDIA	Viva Books Private Limited, 4325/3, Ansari Road, Darya Ganj,
	New Delhi-110002
ISRAEL	YOZMOT Literature Ltd., P.O. Box 56055, IL-61560 Tel Aviv
ITALY	Libreria Scientifica Dott. Lucio di Biasio "AEIOU",
	Via Coronelli 6, I-20146 Milan
JAPAN	Maruzen Company, Ltd., P.O. Box 5050, 100-31 Tokyo International
NETHERLANDS	Martinus Nijhoff International, P.O. Box 269, NL-2501 AX The Hague
	Swets and Zeitlinger b.v., P.O. Box 830, NL-2610 SZ Lisse
POLAND	Ars Polona, Foreign Trade Enterprise,
	Krakowskie Przedmieście 7, PL-00-068 Warsaw
SLOVAKIA	Alfa Press Publishers, Hurbanovo námestie 3, SQ-815 89 Bratislava
SPAIN	Díaz de Santos, Lagasca 95, E-28006 Madrid
	Díaz de Santos, Balmes 417, E-08022 Barcelona
SWEDEN	Fritzes Customer Service, S-106 47 Stockholm
UNITED KINGDOM	HMSO, Publications Centre, Agency Section,
	51 Nine Elms Lane, London SW8 5DR

☆ ☆ Orders (except for customers in Canada and the USA) and requests for information may also be addressed directly to:

Sales and Promotion Unit
International Atomic Energy Agency
Wagramerstrasse 5, P.O. Box 100, A-1400 Vienna, Austria

Telephone: +43 1 2060 22529 (or 22530)
Facsimile: +43 1 2060 29302
Electronic mail: SALESPUB@ADPO1.IAEA.OR.AT